The Unseen Spectrum

PHILIP KOGAN, M.Sc.

FOUNDATIONS OF SCIENCE LIBRARY

GREYSTONE PRESS/NEW YORK · TORONTO · LONDON

This new presentation assembles freshly edited material from
'Understanding Science' on one subject into a single volume.

Copyright © MCMLXVI Sampson Low, Marston & Co. Ltd.

Library of Congress Catalog Card Number: 66–17979

Printed in Great Britain
Manufactured in U.S.A.

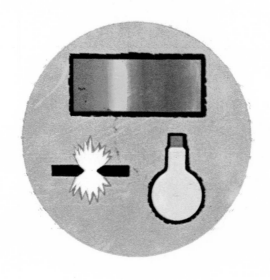

Contents

3

Light and Spectra

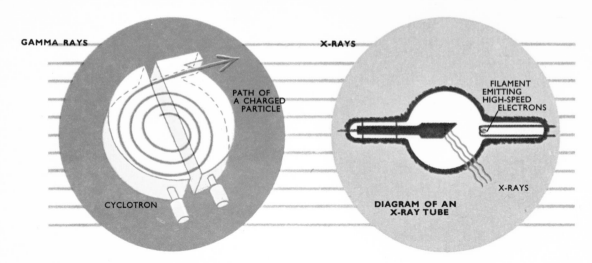

GAMMA RAYS

PATH OF
A CHARGED
PARTICLE

CYCLOTRON

X-RAYS

FILAMENT
EMITTING
HIGH-SPEED
ELECTRONS

X-RAYS

DIAGRAM OF AN
X-RAY TUBE

Gamma rays *are produced by nuclear reactions which may be initiated by particles from a cyclotron.*

Metal target being bombarded with high-speed electrons to produce X-rays.

CHAPTER ONE

Across the Spectrum

THERE seem to be considerable differences between X-rays and radio waves. Both of these appear to differ from gamma (γ) rays (which are penetrating rays which have even been detected after passing through an 8-inch thickness of lead), visible light rays and invisible ultra-violet rays. Yet all of these are similar in character. All are electromagnetic vibrations and over long distances they travel in straight lines. None is deviated from its path by a magnetic field. All travel at the same speed in a vacuum, that of light, 186,000 miles per second, or measured on the metric system, 30,000,000,000 cms./sec. This can be written as 3×10^{10} cms./sec. The only difference between them is that they have different wavelengths.

By passing it through a triangular wedge of glass (prism), ordinary white light can be split up into a whole

Visible light, produced by incandescent lamps and carbon arc lamps.

VISIBLE REGION

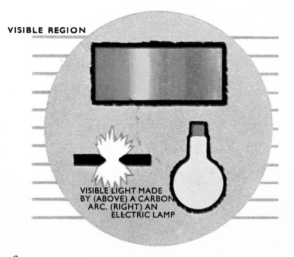

VISIBLE LIGHT MADE
BY (ABOVE) A CARBON
ARC. (RIGHT) AN
ELECTRIC LAMP

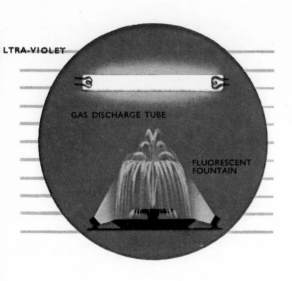

Ultra-violet *radiation being given off in a gas discharge, and causing fluorescence.*

range of colours. The jumbled mixture of wavelengths is sorted into an ordered range and consequently the light separates into its component colours, each colour shade with its own wavelength. This range of colours is known as the visible spectrum.

Because most electromagnetic vibrations are so very small, it is inconvenient to measure their wavelengths in centimetres. The Ångström (Å) is used instead. One Ångström is a hundred millionth of a centimetre, i.e. $\frac{1}{100,000,000}$ or 10^{-8} cms.

Light has wavelengths ranging between 3,800 Å (violet) and 7,600 Å (red light). The other colours of the spectrum have wavelengths somewhere between these two values. But the limit of human vision is by no means the limit of the spectrum. Beyond the violet end of the light spectrum lies the region of ultra-violet, and beyond that are X and gamma rays which are not found by splitting sunlight. Neither are radio waves, which lie well beyond the red end of the spectrum. Ultra-violet rays can have wavelengths from 3,900 Å down to 136 Å. The shorter ultra-violet rays are similar to X-rays, only they are produced by different means. X-rays range from 1,020 Å

Infra-red radiation (heat rays).

Radio waves. Electromagnetic waves are produced by oscillating currents in electric circuits.

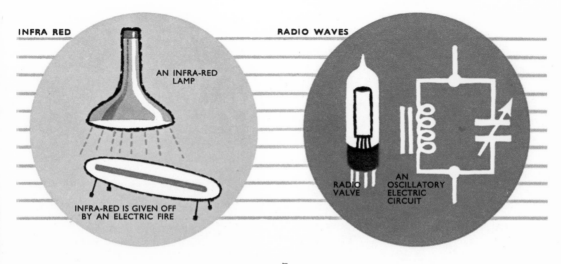

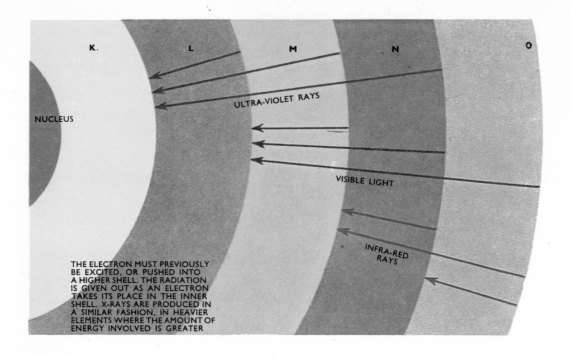

K. L M N O

ULTRA-VIOLET RAYS

NUCLEUS

VISIBLE LIGHT

INFRA-RED RAYS

THE ELECTRON MUST PREVIOUSLY BE EXCITED, OR PUSHED INTO A HIGHER SHELL. THE RADIATION IS GIVEN OUT AS AN ELECTRON TAKES ITS PLACE IN THE INNER SHELL. X-RAYS ARE PRODUCED IN A SIMILAR FASHION, IN HEAVIER ELEMENTS WHERE THE AMOUNT OF ENERGY INVOLVED IS GREATER

to 0·06 Å. Gamma (γ) rays are of even shorter wavelength (1·4–0·01 Å). Ultra-violet, X and gamma rays are all of shorter wavelengths than the visible spectrum. Infra-red and radio waves are of longer wavelength. Infra-red wavelengths vary from 7,700 Å to 4,000,000 or 4×10^6 Å, and radio waves from $2·2 \times 10^6$ Å up to 10^{15} Å (10,000,000 or 10^7 cms.). Radio wavelengths are often measured in metres. For example, a typical radio station transmits on the medium waveband at 208 metres, while another programme may be broadcast on the long waveband at 1,500 metres.

Gamma (*γ*) *rays*, have extremely high energies, so it is not surprising that they are produced by some nuclear reactions. *When one radioactive element changes into another*, changes take place within the nucleus of the atom. For example, when protons (hydrogen ions) are fired at a target of carbon, a proton can enter and become part of the nucleus. The new

heavier atom is an atom of an isotope of nitrogen. But the new nitrogen atom is slightly lighter than the total weights of the carbon atom and proton from which it was formed. Mass appears to have been lost. The lost mass has been converted into energy as gamma radiation. Gamma rays are also given off when some naturally radioactive materials, such as radium, decay. It is the gamma rays that make radium of use in the

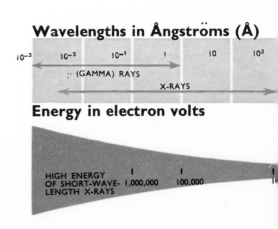

Wavelengths in Ångströms (Å)

10^{-3}	10^{-2}	10^{-1}	1	10	10^2

γ (GAMMA) RAYS

X-RAYS

Energy in electron volts

HIGH ENERGY OF SHORT-WAVE- 1,000,000 100,000 LENGTH X-RAYS

8

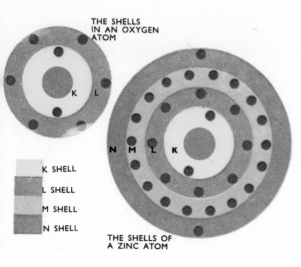

THE SHELLS IN AN OXYGEN ATOM

K SHELL

L SHELL

M SHELL

N SHELL

THE SHELLS OF A ZINC ATOM

Opposite: *Types of radiation given out when electrons fall into shells of lower energy.* Above: *Atoms showing electron shells. They are labelled K, L, M, etc., in the conventional manner.*

works on this principle.

X-rays fall into two categories, *hard* and *soft*. The hard X-rays have high energy and are harmful to the body. They are used in the treatment of cancer. The soft ones with less energy are used in X-ray photography. X-rays are produced in a sealed tube which has been evacuated. X-rays come off when high-speed electrons are fired at a metal target. Whether they are hard or soft depends on the pressure of the small amount of gas remaining in the tube. When the gas pressure is low, a high voltage is needed to operate the tube. The bombarding electrons are of high speed and the X-rays given off are penetrating hard ones of high energy. Higher gas pressures produce soft X-rays. The nucleus of the bombarded atom does not take part in their formation, only the surrounding electrons. The shell of electrons closest to the nucleus is known as the K shell. The L shell is the next, followed by the M and N shells. When a bombarding electron knocks an electron out of the tightly bound inner K shell, the one removed goes into an outer shell and an outer electron moves into the K shell to take its place. In this shell it needs less energy, so the excess is given out as hard X-rays. When the bombarding electron has insufficient energy to remove a K electron it removes an

treatment of cancer. Gamma rays can be *detected* by the *photoelectric effect*. When they are directed on to a special metal plate sealed in a vacuum, the plate gives off some electrons. These are collected by a metal cup and pass round a circuit as an electric current. This effect is not peculiar to gamma radiation. X-rays, ultra-violet, light rays and infra-red radiation all, under the right circumstances, create photoelectricity, and this can be used for their detection. The photographer's light meter

| 10^5 | 10^6 | 10^7 | 10^8 | 10^9 | 10^{10} | 10^{11} | 10^{12} | 10^{13} |

RADIO WAVES

INFRA-RED

AN ELECTRON VOLT IS A CONVENIENT UNIT FOR EXPRESSING THE ENERGIES OF ELECTROMAGNETIC WAVES, OR OF ANY CHARGED ATOMIC PARTICLES. IT IS THE AMOUNT OF ENERGY WHICH AN ELECTRON WOULD HAVE AFTER BEING ACCELERATED THROUGH AN ELECTRICAL PRESSURE DIFFERENCE OF 1 VOLT.

0·01

LOW-ENERGY RADIO WAVES

0·00000001 $\left(\dfrac{1}{100\ MILLION}\right)$

L one instead. An outer electron moving into the gap in the L shell releases less energy, so the X-rays are soft. Like light, X-rays are reflected by mirrors. Crystals of pure salt can be used instead of glass to bend the path of X-rays, sorting them into their different wavelengths. Like light, they blacken a photographic plate, have a photoelectric effect and a slight heating effect on obstacles in their path.

Ultra-violet lamps are quite well known. Because of some visible violet light mixed with it, the radiation has a violet tinge. When it falls on teeth or finger-nails it makes them fluoresce. Ultra-violet rays are absorbed and visible light is emitted. In fluorescent lighting the ultra-violet radiation inside the glass tube excites its lining of fluorescent powder and white light is given out. Ultra-violet radiation is used for killing germs on wounds and for controlling bacteria in food. It is produced by passing an electric discharge through a gas such as mercury vapour at low pressure. Ultra-violet radiation is of less energy and longer wavelength than gamma or X radiation. The electric discharge excites the atoms of gas, giving electrons in the K shell

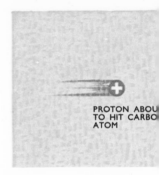

PROTON ABOUT TO HIT CARBON ATOM

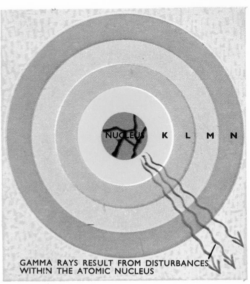

GAMMA RAYS RESULT FROM DISTURBANCES WITHIN THE ATOMIC NUCLEUS

enough energy to jump into an outer shell. They quickly jump back again, and in doing so give out parcels of energy as ultra-violet radiation. Ultra-violet light affects a photographic plate and exhibits a photoelectric effect.

Visible light, ranging from high energy violet to lower energy red, is given out by electrical discharges and by substances at high temperatures. Here again the atoms become excited (in this case by heat). Electrons jump out of the M shell and quickly jump back again, giving out light energy. If they have only jumped back one shell, not much energy will be emitted (red end of the spectrum). If they have jumped back through more

Radio waves are produced by the vibrations of electrons and nuclei in a magnetic or electric field.

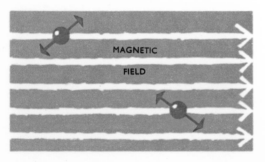

MAGNETIC

FIELD

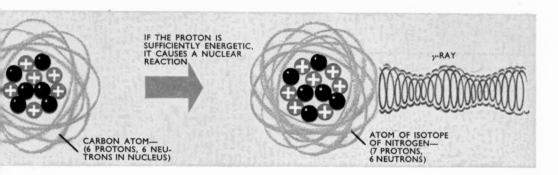

IF THE PROTON IS SUFFICIENTLY ENERGETIC, IT CAUSES A NUCLEAR REACTION

γ-RAY

CARBON ATOM— (6 PROTONS, 6 NEU- TRONS IN NUCLEUS)

ATOM OF ISOTOPE OF NITROGEN— (7 PROTONS, 6 NEUTRONS)

Reactions involving an atomic nucleus sometimes produce gamma rays. This happens when carbon atoms are bombarded with protons.

shells then the light emitted will be at the violet end of the spectrum. The human eye is a good detector of light rays. They affect a photographic plate and also have a heating effect.

Infra-red rays are similar to light rays, only they lie beyond the range of our vision. They are produced by electrons jumping in and out of the M or N shell. The best way of detecting them is by their heating effect, but those nearer the visible end can also be photographed. Although they cannot be seen, photographic plates are sensitive to them.

Radio waves are given out by oscillations in electric circuits and detected by the reverse process of making resonant electric circuits oscillate in time with them. They too can be detected by their heating effect. In an oscillating circuit, charge builds up across a condenser and then discharges into the windings of a choke (coil). Electromagnetic radio waves are given out as the current flows through the choke, producing electromagnetic energy in the core. The alternate charging and discharging of the condenser follow each other in rapid succession, giving rise to radio waves.

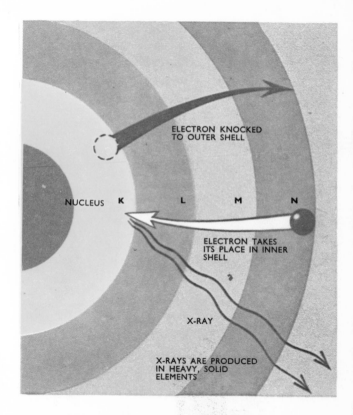

ELECTRON KNOCKED TO OUTER SHELL

NUCLEUS   K   L   M   N

ELECTRON TAKES ITS PLACE IN INNER SHELL

X-RAY

X-RAYS ARE PRODUCED IN HEAVY, SOLID ELEMENTS

Production of hard X-rays. (Soft X-rays are produced by knocking electrons out of the L shell.) X-rays are usually produced by bombarding heavier, solid elements.

CHAPTER TWO

Some Aspects of Visible Radiation

IN the simplest method of producing a spectrum of light, a prism, a block of glass of triangular cross-section, is put in the path of a narrow beam of light. Because each of the different colours of light travels through the prism along slightly different routes, each colour appears at a slightly different position on the other side of the prism. When sunlight, or the light from an incandescent light bulb is viewed in this way, a continuous band of colours, ranging from red, through orange, yellow, green, blue, and indigo to violet is produced. The colours merge gradually into each other.

This is called a *continuous spectrum*. Each colour in it is characterised by its own *wavelength*, for it is known that light is a kind of wave-motion and the colour of light depends on its wavelength. Wavelengths of red light are roughly twice as long as the wavelengths of blue light.

A beam of 'white' light has been divided into its constituent colours, the *continuous spectrum*. The light originates from the hot filament of an electric lamp bulb, so obviously all the different colours of light must have been produced within the filament itself.

When objects are heated very strongly they invariably emit light, and they are said to become *incandescent*. To find out exactly why incandescent substances emit light, it is necessary to examine the behaviour of the building bricks of the filament, the atoms themselves.

The filament, in common with all matter, is made up of atoms, each consisting of a heavy nucleus, surrounded by a much lighter 'cloud' of *electrons*. The electric current flowing

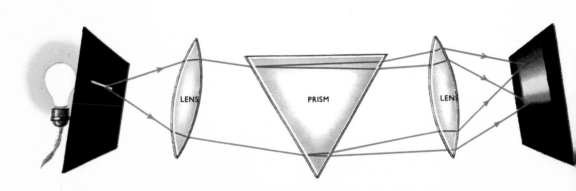

Light is split up into its colours by a prism.

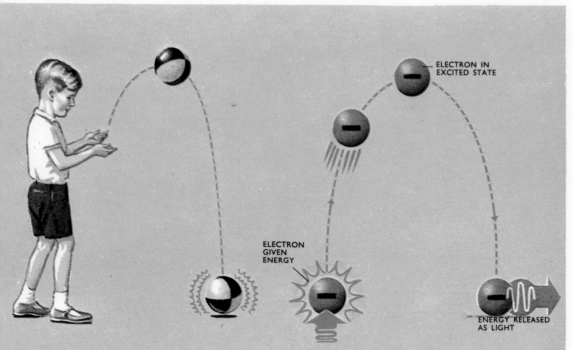

The ball releases energy as it falls to the ground. When an electron 'falls down', it emits its excess energy as a light 'bundle'.

through the filament heats it, and affects the electrons grouped around the nucleus. The electrons most likely to be affected are those farthest away from the nucleus. Not unnaturally, they become 'excited' by the heat from the electric current. The heat gives them an extra amount of energy.

Now that the electrons have more energy, they are able to fly farther away from the atoms to which they are bound. But there they are in an 'excited state' and very unstable. The electrons cannot remain in this state for very long. In fact, their occupation of the 'excited state' lasts for only the tiniest fraction of a second. Almost immediately, they jump back to their normal, unexcited state.

But they have too much energy to be in this state. The excess energy must be discarded before they can remain there.

This process is rather like throwing a ball upwards. Energy is given to the ball (by the thrower), and this energy enables it to move upwards. When it reaches the uppermost point of its path, the ball stays there for an infinitely short time, momentarily suspended in mid-air. The uppermost point of the ball's path is like the 'excited state' of the electron in the lamp filament. The ball drops back and hits the ground. But by the time it hits the ground, it is moving quickly. Before it can remain stationary on the ground, the extra energy must be discarded. Some of it is converted into sound energy, and some, by friction, into heat.

But, it happens that the excess

13

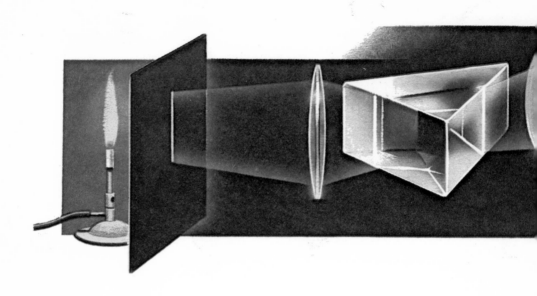

Producing the yellow sodium spectrum.

energy carried by electrons in the lamp filament is emitted as *light energy*. Each excited atom must emit a tiny bundle of it, called a *photon*.

The colour of the light, the wavelength of the light and the size of the bundle of energy are all directly related to each other. For bundles of blue light have more energy than bundles of green light, which in turn have more energy than bundles of red light. In fact, the longer the wavelength (red light has the longest wavelength of visible light) the smaller the energy bundle. So the size of the energy bundle emitted by the excited electron governs the colour of the light it represents.

All the electrons in the heated filament are being excited by slightly different amounts. So they are emitting bundles of energy of different sizes, equivalent to bundles of light of different colours. All these bundles, jumbled together, give the overall impression of white light.

However, not all sources of light are 'white'. Many heated substances do not give out a jumbled 'white' mixture of light. They emit light of a definite colour. In other words, they emit energy in the form of bundles, of certain definite sizes.

If a piece of paper soaked in brine is burnt, it produces a yellow flame. The most predominant light bundles are the ones corresponding to certain wavelengths of yellow light. It is the sodium in the brine which is responsible for this. When the single very close to each other, and easily mistakable for one single one. Each image is caused by light of a different wavelength, brought by the prism to a slightly different position on the screen. These are the two wavelengths emitted by sodium.

Why does the sodium flame give out definite wavelengths, while the lamp filament gives out a jumbled mixture?

One of the reasons is that the atoms making up the lamp filament are very heavy ones, each with a great many electrons. There are many different 'excited ·states' into which they are allowed to go. So bundles of energy of many different sizes can be given out. Another reason is that the atoms

The yellow 'line' can be resolved into two 'lines' with more precise equipment.

electron around each sodium nucleus is excited, it has the choice of only two 'excited states' to go in. These are the only ones allowed – in any other 'excited states' the electron simply could not exist. When it drops back into its normal unexcited state, the electron can emit light bundles of only two different sizes, both corresponding to wavelengths of yellow light.

If light from this sodium flame is first passed through a narrow slit, and then through a prism, each slightly different yellow wavelength takes a slightly different route. The light finally focused on to a screen is in fact the image of a narrow slit. If this experiment is performed with very precise equipment, then two yellow, narrow slit images can be seen, both

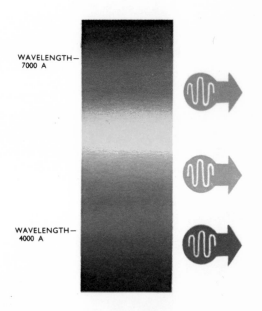

WAVELENGTH—
7000 A

WAVELENGTH—
4000 A

The colour of the light 'bundle', or photon, *depends on its wave-length.*

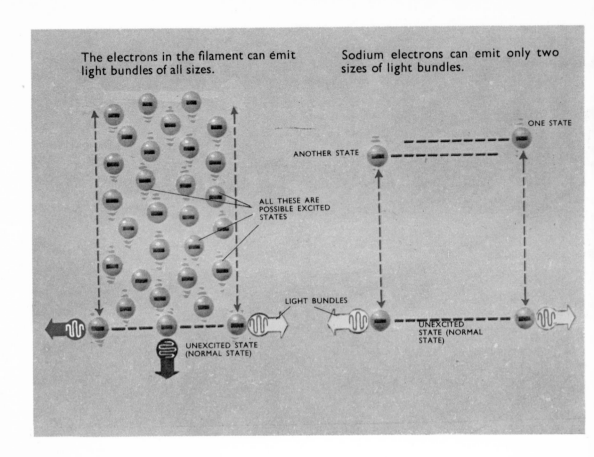

The electrons in the filament can emit light bundles of all sizes.

Sodium electrons can emit only two sizes of light bundles.

ALL THESE ARE POSSIBLE EXCITED STATES

UNEXCITED STATE (NORMAL STATE)

LIGHT BUNDLES

ANOTHER STATE

ONE STATE

UNEXCITED STATE (NORMAL STATE)

in the lamp filament are tightly packed together. The consequence is that outermost electrons are shared partly by one parent nucleus, and partly by another. 'Excited states' of one run into 'excited states' of the other, with the effect that the number of allowed 'excited states' is increased enormously. The excited electrons are capable of emitting bundles of energy corresponding to practically the whole range of colours of the visible spectrum.

CHAPTER THREE

Quanta — Bundles of Energy

IF proof were ever needed that the scientist must always be open-minded and prepared to change his ideas when new facts are discovered, it is to be found in the way that theories of the nature of light have changed through the centuries.

First, it was thought that light was thrown out from a luminous body in the form of light corpuscles – tiny round pellets.

This was believed by the ancient Greeks and the theory still held sway in the time of Sir Isaac Newton, in the seventeenth century. Then, with the demonstration of *interference* of light beams the resemblance to the behaviour of water waves was so strong that

the *wave theory* of light superseded the corpuscular theory.

By the beginning of the twentieth century the wave nature of light had become well established. All the known experimental facts seemed to be fully explained by it. James Clerk Maxwell had shown that light radiation as well as heat radiation consisted of electromagnetic waves. According to the electromagnetic theory a heated body contained a large number of atomic oscillators, which gave out the waves. The greater the frequency of oscillation, the shorter the wavelength of the radiation. The atomic oscillators should give out the waves *continuously*, like the waves given out when a cork is bobbed up and down in a water tank.

Maxwell's theory was expressed in a number of mathematical equations, and these were applied by Lord Rayleigh and Sir James Jeans, who worked out how much energy should be expected to be radiated by a *black body* radiator (a perfect heat absorbing and emitting cavity) at different wavelengths. One of the predictions of the Rayleigh-Jeans law of radiation was that as the wavelength of radiation was made smaller and smaller, the energy of radiation should get larger. The actual radiation law, found by experiment, was in complete disagreement with this conclusion. There was obviously something wrong with the theory that the law was based on.

Then Max Planck in 1900, made a quite revolutionary suggestion – that the radiation was not given out in a continuous train of waves, but in the

Detecting single photons. Very weak beams of light can be detected using a photon-counter. A single photon enters window and strikes the negative central wire. A single electron is dislodged and this passes to the positively charged cylinder. On its way it knocks other electrons out of gas molecules and these form an electron current pulse that can be detected in the external current.

-B

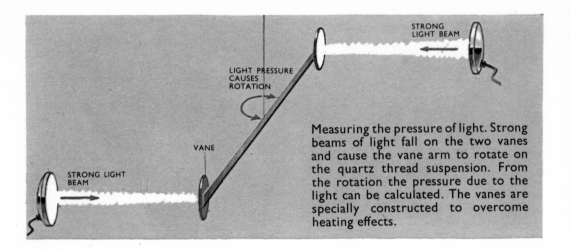

LIGHT PRESSURE
CAUSES
ROTATION

STRONG
LIGHT BEAM

STRONG LIGHT
BEAM

VANE

Measuring the pressure of light. Strong beams of light fall on the two vanes and cause the vane arm to rotate on the quartz thread suspension. From the rotation the pressure due to the light can be calculated. The vanes are specially constructed to overcome heating effects.

form of radiation packets called *quanta*. The atomic oscillators still existed in this theory but they threw out energy in short, sharp, bursts. The energy of each quantum depended on the *frequency* of the radiation – the higher the frequency (i.e. at shorter wavelengths) the greater the energy of each quantum.

These ideas were expressed in mathematical form by Planck and from his equations a new radiation law was worked out. From this, amounts of energy emitted at the different wavelengths was predicted. The predictions, based on Planck's theory, corresponded well with the results found from experiment. So the quantum theory of radiation was verified.

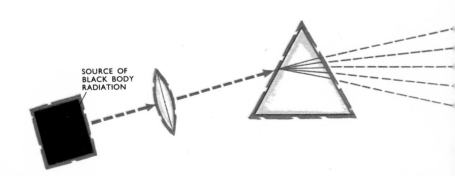

SOURCE OF
BLACK BODY
RADIATION

Finding the change in radiation energy with change in wavelength. The heat radiation is given out by a black body radiator and is split into the different wavelengths by the lens and prism (spectrometer). The thermopile is moved along to pick up the different wavelength radiations and the meter reading indicates the energy of the radiation at each position. The energy is plotted against wavelength on a graph. The experimental (full-line) curve is in accordance with Planck's theory – the wave theory would lead to the dotted line curve, not found in practice.

The Theory of Specific Heat

After Planck's success in explaining black body radiation, his theory was applied to a number of other physical facts that needed clarification. One of these was the variation of specific heat of materials with temperature. Beforehand, it had been assumed that as a mass of material was heated up, the heat energy was absorbed by the solid, and the molecules in the solid took up the energy by vibrating with vibrations of increased amplitude. The amount of heat energy absorbed by a gram of the material for one degree rise in temperature is called the *specific heat*. If each particle simply vibrates more and more vigorously with a rise in temperature there is no reason to expect that the specific heat would change with a rise in temperature. The heat needed to raise one gram of copper from 19°C to 20°C should be the same as that needed to raise it from 99°C to 100°C. The experimental results of measurements of specific heats showed, in fact, that specific heat did change with a change in temperature, so the simple theory of the continuously vibrating particle could not be correct.

Then Albert Einstein suggested that the heat energy possessed by the particles must be in the form, once again, of energy packets – quanta. A mathematical equation that expressed this idea was worked out, and the change in specific heat with temperature was predicted from this equation. The predicted results were found to correspond to the results found by experiment. Once again the idea that energy exists in the form of quanta was verified.

The Photoelectric Effect

When light falls on a metal surface electrons can sometimes be dislodged. This is the *photoelectric effect*. The energy of the dislodged electrons can quite easily be studied in the laboratory. The results of such experiments were studied by Albert Einstein. One result that caught his attention was that even when a very weak beam of light was used, an electron was sometimes emitted. Sometimes this would happen quickly and other times there would be a long interval before the electron was dislodged. Einstein pointed out that this result could only be explained if the light was in the form of quanta, (called *photons*). If the light were in the form of a wave, the energy would be spread evenly over a large area, and in some of the experiments it would take much longer to dislodge an electron than was actually the case. So once again the quantum theory was able to explain an experi-

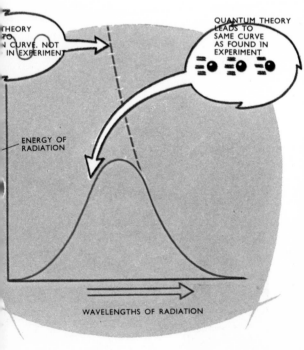

QUANTUM THEORY LEADS TO SAME CURVE AS FOUND IN EXPERIMENT

THEORY TO CURVE. NOT IN EXPERIMENT

ENERGY OF RADIATION

WAVELENGTHS OF RADIATION

mental result that the classical theory could not.

The Pressure of Light

The application of the quantum theory of energy was very successful in explaining black body radiation, specific heats, and the photoelectric effect. In all of these examples the theory had to be applied through the use of mathematical equations. It is also possible to show, by means of a fairly simple experiment, that light consists of a stream of particle-like bundles of energy.

One would expect that a succession of such bundles would exert a pressure on a surface just as moving molecules in a gas exert pressure on the walls of a container. The pressure of light has been demonstrated in a laboratory experiment. The apparatus used has to be very sensitive because the actual pressure is only $\dfrac{1}{1,000,000}$ dyne per square centimetre.

Two vanes are attached to the ends of a bar, and the bar is suspended, at its mid point, from a fine quartz fibre. Light from two powerful sources strikes the surface of the vanes so that the bar rotates. From the amount of rotation the pressure of the light is calculated. The vane surfaces are carefully constructed to eliminate the effects of heating due to the absorption of light. (The air molecules near a heated surface move faster than those at an unheated surface so they exert extra pressure.)

Counting Photons

Individual light quanta (photons) may be counted using an electronic counter. In this, a photon strikes a metal wire and releases an electron by photo-emission. The wire is sealed in the chamber along the axis of a metal cylinder, and a voltage difference is maintained between the wire and the cylinder. The released electron passes to the positive cylinder and in doing so releases more electrons as, en route, it ionizes gas molecules. A small avalanche of electrons is formed and this produces a current pulse that can be detected by an electronic circuit. By adjusting the voltage difference between the wire and the cylinder, the cell can be made to give one current pulse for each photon that enters. So, individual photons can be detected and counted.

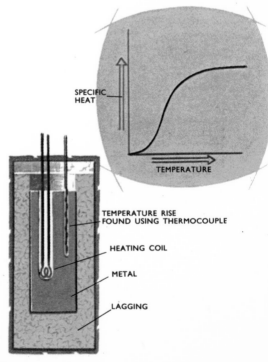

The specific heat of a solid at different temperatures can be found by measuring the rise in temperature when a known amount of heat is absorbed by the solid from a heating coil. If the results of such experiments are plotted on a graph the curve shown results. These results can only be explained by the quantum theory of specific heats — the older theories predict a straight horizontal line curve.

SPECIFIC HEAT

TEMPERATURE

TEMPERATURE RISE FOUND USING THERMOCOUPLE

HEATING COIL

METAL

LAGGING

CHAPTER FOUR

The Spectrum — Energy Chart of the Molecule

WHEN a tuning fork is struck, it gives out a musical note of definite pitch (*frequency*). The energy of the blow is absorbed by the prongs and the fork gets rid of some of this energy by vibrating and setting up a train of sound waves. By listening to the sound, it would be possible to find out quite a lot about the tuning fork. The frequency of the sound is the same as the rate of vibration of the prongs. If the fork gives out low notes, it must be a big fork with heavy prongs; if a high note, the prongs must be small and light so that they can vibrate more quickly.

The way the prongs vibrate can be studied very easily by taking a slow motion film. But the behaviour of an atom or molecule cannot be examined in this way, even under the most powerful microscope. The behaviour of the tiny atom is made apparent by 'striking' the atom and sampling the 'note' that is given out. The atom is struck by a moving electron, and the energy given out is in the form of light waves, not musical notes. By studying the light waves, a lot can be learned about the atom or molecule that is giving it out.

The spectrum of an atom or molecule can be produced by passing an electrical discharge through a specimen of the gas. In the discharge, electrons collide with the atoms and excite them so that they give out light. The light given out is normally a complicated mixture of different colours or wavelengths. These might range right through the visible spectrum, from red to violet, or might be in the invisible ultra-violet or infra-red regions. By sorting out the spectrum of a molecule the spectroscopist can learn a great deal about the structure and behaviour of the molecule. In fact, the science of spectroscopy has provided us with a great deal of vital information about the structure of matter.

When a tuning fork is banged on a table it gives out a pure musical note. The sound is carried because a train of compression waves passes through the air. These waves are picked up by the microphone and produce a wave pattern on the cathode ray oscilloscope.

PURE MUSICAL NOTE GIVES REGULAR WAVEFORM

NOISE OF STONE GIVES JUMBLED PATTERN

When a stone is thrown at a metal oil-can it gives out a sound because the metal surface vibrates. The sound is a jumbled mixture of musical notes, and the wave trace on the oscilloscope is an irregular pattern. This mixture of notes is found to be always the same for the particular can.

Wavelength and Energy

Light can be split into its different colours by passing it through a *spectroscope*. In its simplest form this consists of a glass or quartz prism. This produces a spectrum of the light, which is simply a display of all the colours present, arranged in order of wavelength. Now the shorter the wavelength of the light, the greater its energy. For example, green light is of greater energy than yellow light, because yellow light has the greater wavelength. If one substance in a discharge tube gives out green light and another yellow light, it means that the first type of atom is giving out more energy than the second.

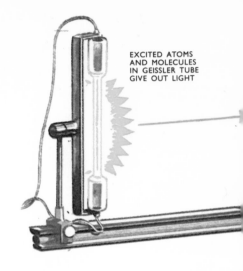

EXCITED ATOMS AND MOLECULES IN GEISSLER TUBE GIVE OUT LIGHT

Electronic Spectra

What sorts of energy changes (*transitions*) might be expected in a molecule of hydrogen gas in a discharge tube? The first sort is *electronic excitation*. The electrons in a molecule occupy orbits around the positively charged nuclei of the molecule. When they receive energy they are knocked into an orbit further from the nucleus. When an electron returns to its original orbit, it gives up this energy as light of a quite definite wavelength. By measuring the wavelength of the light, the differences in energy of the electrons in orbits in an atom or molecule are easily found.

When all the light given out is due to electronic excitation alone, the spectrum consists of sets of quite distinct lines. This is the *line spectrum*. The whole pattern of lines in an electronic spectrum will provide very complete information about the electron orbits in the atom or molecule. It is found that electrons can only take up very definite orbits in a particular atom or molecule, and the energies of the electron in these orbits can be worked out very accurately from the positions of the lines in the spectrum.

The Vibrational Spectrum

If the spectrum of a molecule like nitrogen or hydrogen is examined, it will be seen that it is made up of a series of bands. The line spectrum of an atom is caused by an energy change

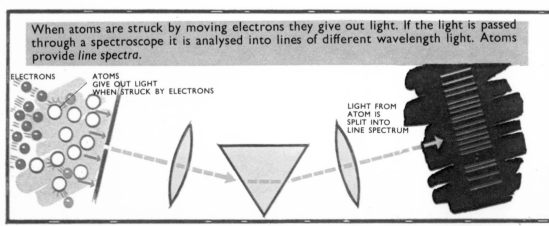

When atoms are struck by moving electrons they give out light. If the light is passed through a spectroscope it is analysed into lines of different wavelength light. Atoms provide *line spectra*.

ELECTRONS

ATOMS GIVE OUT LIGHT WHEN STRUCK BY ELECTRONS

LIGHT FROM ATOM IS SPLIT INTO LINE SPECTRUM

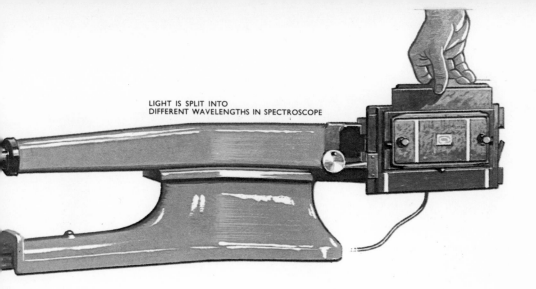

LIGHT IS SPLIT INTO
DIFFERENT WAVELENGTHS IN SPECTROSCOPE

involving the electrons around the nuclei. The band spectrum is caused by energy given out when the nuclei in a molecule vibrate. The nuclei pulsate to and fro with the distance between them varying. A series of bands is formed by different molecules absorbing different amounts of energy in the discharge tube and emitting various wavelengths. The band spectrum of a particular type of molecule is always the same because the different amounts of energy that can be given out are rigidly defined – just as a tuning fork will give out only a definite fundamental note. The same tuning fork always gives out the same sound and the same molecule gives

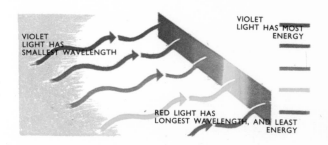

VIOLET
LIGHT HAS
SMALLEST WAVELENGTH

VIOLET
LIGHT HAS MOST
ENERGY

RED LIGHT HAS
LONGEST WAVELENGTH, AND LEAST
ENERGY

Light of different colours has different wavelengths. Red light has the longest wavelength and blue light the shortest, in the visible spectrum. The longer the wavelength of the light, the less its energy. The energies of the light of different colours can be shown on an energy diagram.

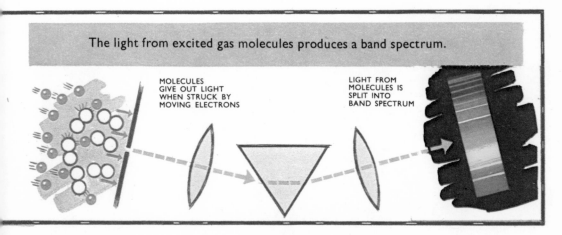

The light from excited gas molecules produces a band spectrum.

MOLECULES
GIVE OUT LIGHT
WHEN STRUCK BY
MOVING ELECTRONS

LIGHT FROM
MOLECULES IS
SPLIT INTO
BAND SPECTRUM

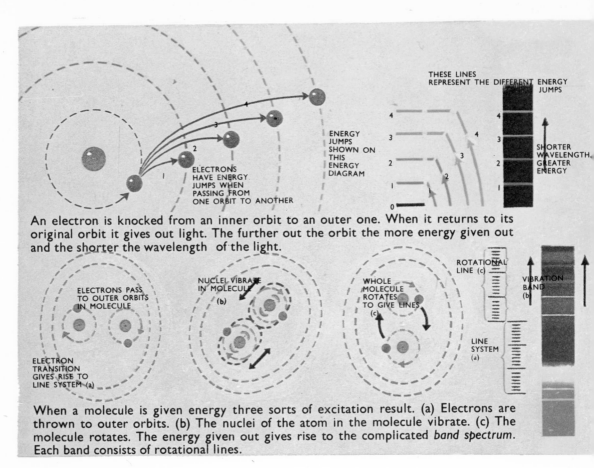

An electron is knocked from an inner orbit to an outer one. When it returns to its original orbit it gives out light. The further out the orbit the more energy given out and the shorter the wavelength of the light.

When a molecule is given energy three sorts of excitation result. (a) Electrons are thrown to outer orbits. (b) The nuclei of the atom in the molecule vibrate. (c) The molecule rotates. The energy given out gives rise to the complicated *band spectrum*. Each band consists of rotational lines.

out the same spectrum. The vibrational spectrum is superimposed on the electronic spectrum so any particular band in it represents the combined effects of the energy from an excited electron and that from the vibrating nuclei.

Light is given out when an electron excited to an outer orbit, or a vibrating or rotating molecule returns to its *ground state*. The wavelength of the light depends on the difference in energy between the excited level and the ground state. There is a complicated mixture of wavelengths given out by the excited molecules but the wavelengths are fixed because only certain energy jumps are possible. These are called *allowed transitions* and the wavelengths due to allowed transitions can be worked out from theory.

By studying band spectra of molecules information is gained about the forces that bind the atoms together in a molecule.

Rotational Spectrum

The bands of the spectrum are made up of fine lines. These are created by light energy given out when the molecules *rotate*. Once again the rotational energies are fixed for a particular molecule. So the sets of rotational lines in the bands are always in the same position in the spectrum.

The rotational energy of any body depends on its size, mass, and shape and this is as true of a molecule as it is of a spinning top. So from the rotational spectrum the length of the chemical bonds between atoms in molecules is found.

CHAPTER FIVE

Spinning Electrons Split Lines

WHENEVER light is given out by a substance, it means that the atoms or molecules of the substance are throwing out energy. The atom throws out light waves when it is energized just as a bell throws out sound energy when it is struck by a hammer. The wavelength of the light is always the same for a particular atom, in the same way as the note of the bell is always the same.

This is because the light is given out when the electrons, all arranged in fixed orbits, are 'kicked' from one orbit to another. When they return to their original orbits they give out the light.

An electrical discharge is passed through a tube containing atoms of a gas or vapour like sodium or hydrogen.

The atoms are excited by the fast-moving electrons in the discharge and give out light. Sodium and hydrogen atoms have one thing in common – they both have only one electron in their outer orbits. It is normally only the electrons of atoms in the outer orbit that are *excited* and pass out into orbits even further out from the nucleus. These electrons then return to the original orbit, throwing out light waves as they do so. There are a number of different orbits that excited electrons can pass to, and for each of these, light of a different wavelength is given out. If the light is passed through a spectroscope, the light of each of these different *transitions* gives rise to a *line* in the spectrum. In a mass of gas the mixture of different transi-

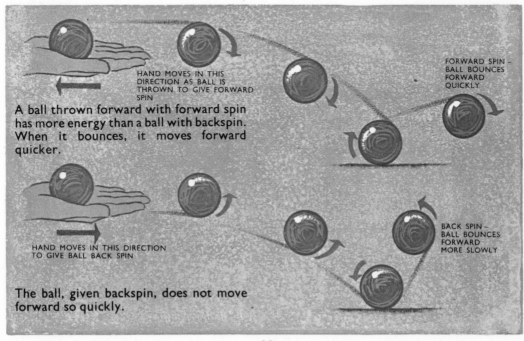

HAND MOVES IN THIS DIRECTION AS BALL IS THROWN TO GIVE FORWARD SPIN

FORWARD SPIN – BALL BOUNCES FORWARD QUICKLY

A ball thrown forward with forward spin has more energy than a ball with backspin. When it bounces, it moves forward quicker.

HAND MOVES IN THIS DIRECTION TO GIVE BALL BACK SPIN

BACK SPIN – BALL BOUNCES FORWARD MORE SLOWLY

The ball, given backspin, does not move forward so quickly.

tions, some from one group of atoms and some from another, give rise to a *series* of lines, spread across the spectrum.

Each line represents an energy change, the difference in energy of the electrons in the original and temporary orbits. But the energy of the electron can be slightly changed by a number of factors, apart from the energies in the different orbits. One of these is *electron spin*. While in orbit, the electron spins on its own axis, rather like a top. The energy due to the spin of the electron makes a contribution to the total energy of the electron.

Now there are two possible directions that a top or an electron can spin, clockwise or anticlockwise. When an electron spinning in one direction passes from one orbit to another it means that the atom must have received a certain amount of energy.

If the electron is spinning in the opposite direction, the amount of energy is slightly different. As a result, the wavelength of light given out in the two different atoms is very slightly different, when the electron returns to its original orbit.

This gives rise to twin lines in the spectrum of atoms like sodium and hydrogen. These *doublets* can be seen as two finely separated lines. When the wavelengths of the lines are worked out from the photographs, it is found that the differences between the twins is very small. For example the well-known sodium twins are of wavelength 5890Å and 5896Å, a difference of 6Å

The doublet lines in the spectrum of hydrogen are even closer together – separated by only 1·59Å. Spectroscopes with high resolving power are used to obtain lines like these, clearly separated.

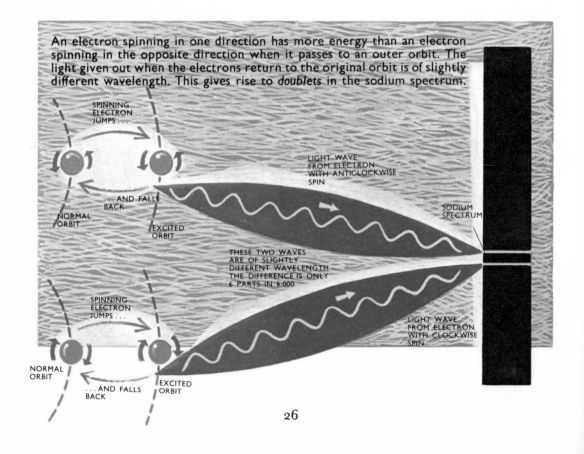

An electron spinning in one direction has more energy than an electron spinning in the opposite direction when it passes to an outer orbit. The light given out when the electrons return to the original orbit is of slightly different wavelength. This gives rise to *doublets* in the sodium spectrum.

SPINNING ELECTRON JUMPS . . .

LIGHT WAVE FROM ELECTRON WITH ANTICLOCKWISE SPIN

. . . AND FALLS BACK

NORMAL ORBIT

EXCITED ORBIT

SODIUM SPECTRUM

THESE TWO WAVES ARE OF SLIGHTLY DIFFERENT WAVELENGTH THE DIFFERENCE IS ONLY 6 PARTS IN 6,000

SPINNING ELECTRON JUMPS . . .

LIGHT WAVE FROM ELECTRON WITH CLOCKWISE SPIN

NORMAL ORBIT

. . . AND FALLS BACK

EXCITED ORBIT

CHAPTER SIX

Absorption and Emission Spectra

ABSORPTION

Absorption spectrum of sodium. The substance under test absorbs certain wavelengths of the radiation beamed through it. Sometimes the absorption is in the visible region of the spectrum. It can also be in the invisible infra-red and ultra-violet regions and right down to micro-waves.

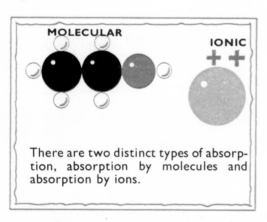

There are two distinct types of absorption, absorption by molecules and absorption by ions.

WHENEVER an atom is given sufficient energy, it starts to give out radiation. Heating the metal sodium makes it give out yellow light. The light is always yellow and consists of light of very definite wavelengths. Under no circumstances will the light of heated sodium appear purple or green. Heating will make the yellow brighter but it will never change the colour.

The reason for this lies in the

EMISSION

Emission spectrum of sodium. When heated, sodium vapour emits double lines of yellow light. The wavelengths are very nearly equal and the lines are very close together.

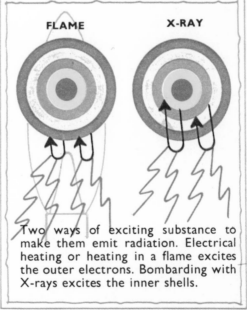

Two ways of exciting substance to make them emit radiation. Electrical heating or heating in a flame excites the outer electrons. Bombarding with X-rays excites the inner shells.

structure of the sodium atoms. A sodium atom has a central nucleus and around it are three layers or shells of electrons. To shift an electron out of one shell into another shell further out, a certain amount of energy is required. The electron cannot stay in the region between shells. It must

27

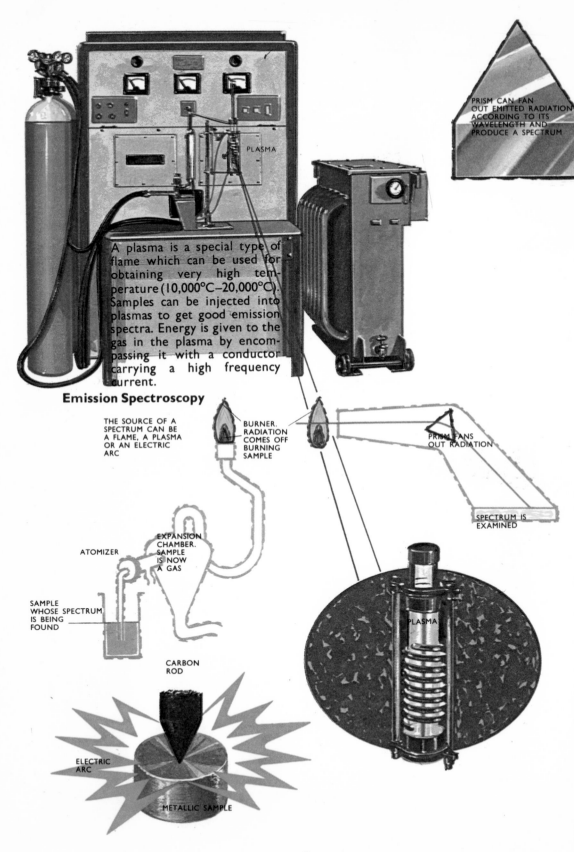

PRISM CAN FAN OUT EMITTED RADIATION ACCORDING TO ITS WAVELENGTH AND PRODUCE A SPECTRUM

PLASMA

A plasma is a special type of flame which can be used for obtaining very high temperature (10,000°C–20,000°C). Samples can be injected into plasmas to get good emission spectra. Energy is given to the gas in the plasma by encompassing it with a conductor carrying a high frequency current.

Emission Spectroscopy

THE SOURCE OF A SPECTRUM CAN BE A FLAME, A PLASMA OR AN ELECTRIC ARC

BURNER. RADIATION COMES OFF BURNING SAMPLE

PRISM FANS OUT RADIATION

SPECTRUM IS EXAMINED

EXPANSION CHAMBER. SAMPLE IS NOW A GAS

ATOMIZER

SAMPLE WHOSE SPECTRUM IS BEING FOUND

PLASMA

CARBON ROD

ELECTRIC ARC

METALLIC SAMPLE

28

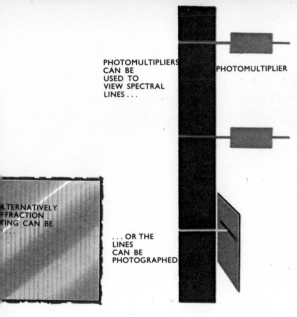

PHOTOMULTIPLIERS CAN BE USED TO VIEW SPECTRAL LINES . . .

PHOTOMULTIPLIER

ALTERNATIVELY DIFFRACTION GRATING CAN BE . . .

. . . OR THE LINES CAN BE PHOTOGRAPHED

is sufficient to shift the electron in the outer (valency) shell. With its extra bundle of energy the electron jumps to a higher energy shell.

It does not stay there long for the electron is excited and unstable, but rapidly jumps back into its old position, getting rid of the extra bundle of energy. Every time an electron jumps back into its old position a definite bundle or *photon* of light energy comes off. Because the light has a certain energy it is always light of a particular colour and wavelength.

There are two possible parcels of energy because sodium electrons come in two types, spinning round in opposite directions and therefore there are two possible positions into which the valency electron can jump (see chapter 5). One has slightly more energy

have enough energy to jump right across from shell to shell. Consequently, the energy involved comes in small parcels – just enough to cause a jump. When sodium is heated, it absorbs a parcel of heat energy which

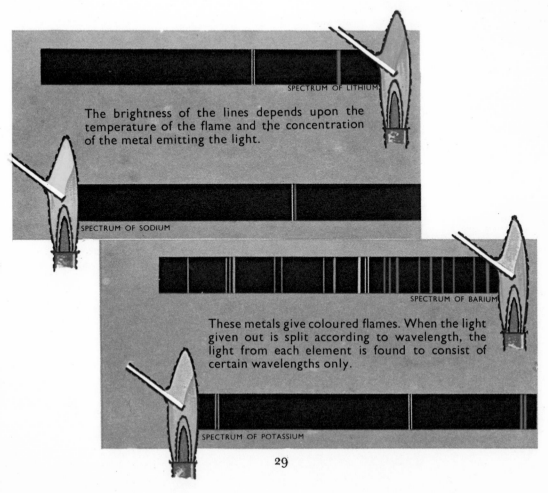

The brightness of the lines depends upon the temperature of the flame and the concentration of the metal emitting the light.

SPECTRUM OF LITHIUM

SPECTRUM OF SODIUM

SPECTRUM OF BARIUM

These metals give coloured flames. When the light given out is split according to wavelength, the light from each element is found to consist of certain wavelengths only.

SPECTRUM OF POTASSIUM

29

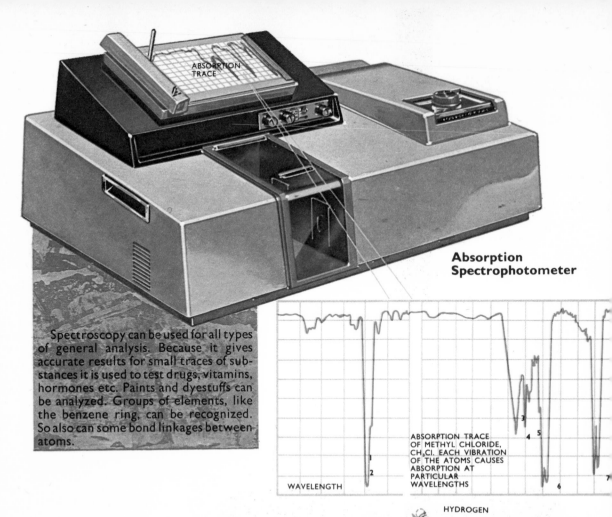

ABSORPTION
TRACE

**Absorption
Spectrophotometer**

ABSORPTION TRACE
OF METHYL CHLORIDE,
CH,CI. EACH VIBRATION
OF THE ATOMS CAUSES
ABSORPTION AT
PARTICULAR
WAVELENGTHS

WAVELENGTH

Spectroscopy can be used for all types of general analysis. Because it gives accurate results for small traces of substances it is used to test drugs, vitamins, hormones etc. Paints and dyestuffs can be analyzed. Groups of elements, like the benzene ring, can be recognized. So also can some bond linkages between atoms.

than the other. Therefore, on jumping back, two different sized bundles of energy are released and light of two slightly different wavelengths is produced. There are some other possible positions into which electrons can jump and thus some other wavelengths of light are also given out.

When sodium light is beamed through a slit on to the side of a prism, the two different wavelengths take slightly different paths. Two yellow images of the slit are obtained, one for each wavelength. The spectrum shows two yellow lines very close to one another. Whenever these two lines appear in a spectrum there must be sodium in the flame.

This is the pattern for sodium, but every single element is built up in its own particular way. Some have

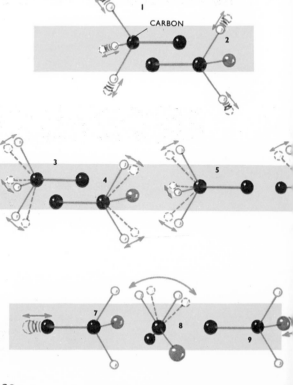

HYDROGEN

CARBON

Absorption Spectrophotometer

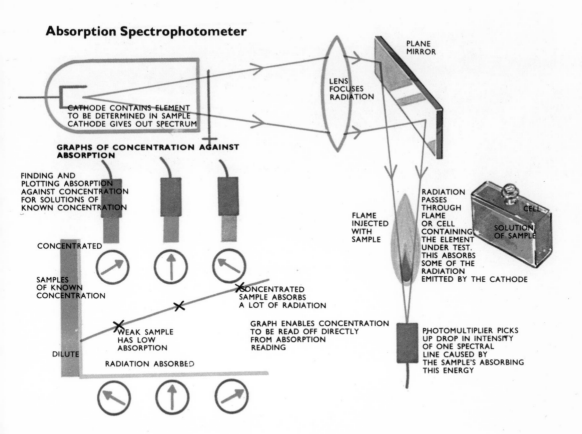

CATHODE CONTAINS ELEMENT TO BE DETERMINED IN SAMPLE CATHODE GIVES OUT SPECTRUM

PLANE MIRROR

LENS FOCUSES RADIATION

GRAPHS OF CONCENTRATION AGAINST ABSORPTION

FINDING AND PLOTTING ABSORPTION AGAINST CONCENTRATION FOR SOLUTIONS OF KNOWN CONCENTRATION

CONCENTRATED

SAMPLES OF KNOWN CONCENTRATION

DILUTE

WEAK SAMPLE HAS LOW ABSORPTION

CONCENTRATED SAMPLE ABSORBS A LOT OF RADIATION

GRAPH ENABLES CONCENTRATION TO BE READ OFF DIRECTLY FROM ABSORPTION READING

RADIATION ABSORBED

RADIATION PASSES THROUGH FLAME OR CELL CONTAINING THE ELEMENT UNDER TEST. THIS ABSORBS SOME OF THE RADIATION EMITTED BY THE CATHODE

FLAME INJECTED WITH SAMPLE

CELL

SOLUTION OF SAMPLE

PHOTOMULTIPLIER PICKS UP DROP IN INTENSITY OF ONE SPECTRAL LINE CAUSED BY THE SAMPLE'S ABSORBING THIS ENERGY

---

more electrons; others have less. Some have more electron shells; others have less. Different sized bundles of energy are required to make different electrons jump into different energy states. The bundles of energy are given out when the electrons jump back again. Each type of atom will give out radiation of particular wavelengths and this will differ from the light wavelengths given out by any other element. Finding the spectrum, then, is a sure means of finger-printing an element.

Heating gives only sufficient energy to shift the outermost electrons. More energy is needed to remove an electron from an inner shell. The nearer the nucleus, the more difficult its removal. When inner electrons are disturbed, a fresh part of the spectrum appears,

again a spectrum characteristic of the particular atom. To shift electrons from inner shells, something with more energy than heat radiation is needed. Bombardment with X-rays will do this.

There are many ways of making elements emit light – heating them, shining other kinds of radiation on them, bombarding with X-rays or other particles. All these are ways of giving the electrons more energy. Because radiation is given out, the spectra produced by both of these methods are known as *emission spectra*.

There is another type of spectrum, an *absorption spectrum*. This time the element under test is made to absorb radiation instead of giving it out. When sodium is under test, a yellow sodium light is produced and is

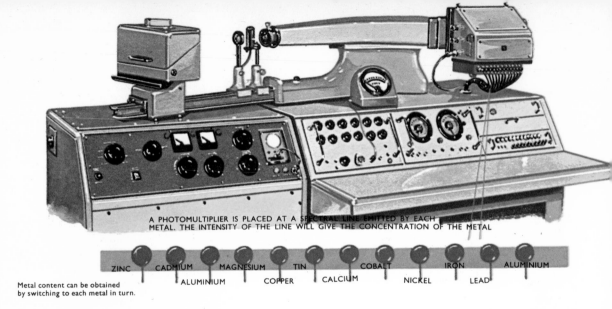

A PHOTOMULTIPLIER IS PLACED AT A SPECTRAL LINE EMITTED BY EACH
METAL. THE INTENSITY OF THE LINE WILL GIVE THE CONCENTRATION OF THE METAL

Metal content can be obtained
by switching to each metal in turn.

ZINC   CADMIUM   MAGNESIUM   TIN   COBALT   IRON   ALUMINIUM

ALUMINIUM   COPPER   CALCIUM   NICKEL   LEAD

directed so that it shines through a glass-walled compartment containing some sodium ions in solution or through a flame into which the sodium sample is injected. The yellow light hits the sample of sodium. It is of just the right energy to excite the atoms. Consequently the sodium absorbs this energy to energize its electrons. The electrons cannot stay in an excited state for long and rapidly revert back to their normal state, emitting the parcels of light they have absorbed. But instead of being emitted in one direction, this light is scattered in all directions. The instrument picks up only a fraction of it. The fraction picked up is now dimmer because most of the light has been scattered in other directions. If there is a lot of sodium in solution, much of the yellow light is much dimmer. If there is only a little, the light intensity is not much affected.

The light emerging from the solution is split up with a prism and examined again to find how the intensity of the 'lines' has been altered.

A source of energy is the first part of any instrument. If the energy given

out by this source is allowed to vary, there will be no point in measuring the intensity at the other end of the spectroscope. It will be constantly changing with the energy source. For intensity measurements to have any meaning at all and be a measure of the quantity of the elements present, the energy must not be allowed to vary at all.

This was the reason the early spectroscopes failed. The spectroscopes of the late 19th century were unreliable because the light sources flickered. In the 20th century, with the advent of more reliable electrical equipment, the spectroscope became an instrument that could be trusted. X-ray machines could work at constant energy. Flames were produced so that their temperatures could not vary. Electric arcs of constant energy were designed. In one of these light sources, electric current is made to jump a gap between a carbon electrode and another electrode made of a metal under test. The light given out as the current jumps the gap is then analyzed to find the metal content of this electrode.

CHAPTER SEVEN

Phosphors and Fluorescence

PHOSPHORS are man-made substances which share with fireflies, glow-worms and various marine animals the ability to give off 'cold' light.

Phosphors are a comparatively recent discovery and were first used extensively in *fluorescent* lamps about 20 years ago. Nowadays their largest

The inside of the face of a television tube is coated with a phosphor. A carefully measured quantity of phosphor powder suspension is introduced into each tube before processing.

application is in strip lighting, television tubes, and in X-ray screens and instruments for research in atomic physics. They are mainly inorganic solids, often in powder form.

The commonest phosphor is zinc sulphide, which forms the main ingredient of the coatings inside television tubes. When struck by electrons, which are accelerated across the tube from the cathode, the coating lights up but does not become very hot. This is a typical example of a phosphor

in action.

Phosphors are really *semiconductors*. These are solids, more often than not, which just conduct electricity. Semiconductors do not conduct electricity as easily as metals such as copper, but they are better conductors than are *insulators*, such as rubber. They come somewhere in between.

Like the semiconductors used in transistors, phosphors depend for their action on the presence of impurities in them. These impurities are not only the secret of phosphors' light-giving action; they also to a large extent control the colour of the light emitted. For instance, the mineral *willemite*, (anhydrous zinc silicate Zn_2SiO_4), has manganese as an impurity. It is this which is responsible for the green light given off.

Phosphors are prepared by heat treatment. The ingredients are mixed together with the small but necessary impurity, and fired in a furnace. All other impurities are rigorously excluded. The firing makes the phosphor crystalline and puts the impurity firmly into the crystal structure. The result is a dry powder, the phosphor, which, in the case of zinc sulphide, looks like cake flour.

Phosphors have to be fired before use. A test sample is being fired in a 1400°C furnace.

How are Phosphors excited?

There are several ways of exciting phosphors so that they emit light. In all of them the phosphor receives energy in one form or other, and emits energy in the form of light of the required wave-length.

For example, ultra-violet light is a similar form of energy to visible light (both are electromagnetic waves), but the wave-lengths of ultra-violet light are shorter than those of visible light. It also has more *energy* because the shorter the wave-length of light, the

greater its energy. When ultra-violet light falls on a phosphor, the high energy ultra-violet light is absorbed, and visible light of lower energy emitted. The difference between the energy absorbed and the energy emitted is wasted in heating up the phosphor, but the effect is to make visible light which otherwise could not be seen.

This may be explained in terms of electron jumps. We can think of electrons moving around the nucleus of an atom in definite orbits, each orbit representing a definite energy level. In a solid, the atoms are close together, and the energy levels of individual atoms combine to form energy *bands*. When ultra-violet light is received by the solid, some of the energy is used in making electrons move from a low energy band to a higher energy band and the rest is used in heating up the phosphor. An electron does not stay in the higher band very long, and it returns to its original band, giving out a burst of energy in the form of visible light.

Different phosphors give off light

34

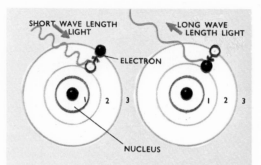

SHORT WAVE LENGTH
LIGHT

LONG WAVE
LENGTH LIGHT

ELECTRON

NUCLEUS

(Left) An electron is shifted from an inner orbit to an outer orbit when it is 'excited' by a light ray.
(Right) Almost immediately, it returns to its original orbit giving out light which is of longer wave length than the original ray.

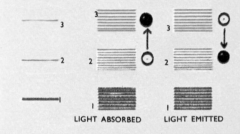

LIGHT ABSORBED   LIGHT EMITTED

(Above) The energies of electrons in atoms may be represented on an energy diagram. The differences in energy of electrons in different orbits is then the distance between the lines on the diagram. In a solid, when a great number of atoms are brought together the energy lines thicken into bands. When energy is absorbed by the solid, an electron may pass from, say, band (2) to band (3). When the electron returns to band 2, light is emitted.

consumed in heating up the phosphor, but a major portion is used in exciting electrons to higher energy levels, so that visible light is emitted when they fall back to their normal energy levels.

A third effect occurring in a solid phosphor is known as *electroluminescence*. The phosphor material is in the form of a thin sandwich about a quarter of an inch thick. One side is glass specially treated to make it conduct electricity. On the other side is a thin aluminium foil. An alternating voltage is applied to the plates on either side of the phosphor. An alternating current, consisting of electrons flowing first one way then the other, flows in the phosphor.

As the free electrons flow, they kick the electrons in the phosphor to a higher level. In between these kicks the phosphor 'relaxes', and its electrons drop back into lower levels, thus releasing light. In this instance, the energy of the electrons in the alternating current is turned into light. The colour of the light given off depends

The colour and light output of phosphors is tested by examination under ultra-violet light of different wavelengths.

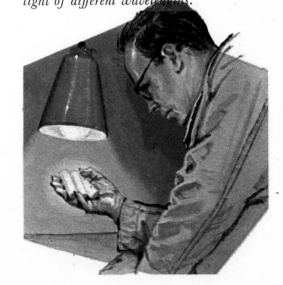

of different colours. This is because the electrons fall back through a definite 'distance' in a particular phosphor. This 'distance' determines the wave-length of the light emitted. In practice, phosphors are mixed in fluorescent lamps, to produce a material which gives off a mixture of colours similar to daylight.

In a television tube, the energy is carried to the phosphor by fast moving electrons accelerated from the cathode. Once again, some of the energy is

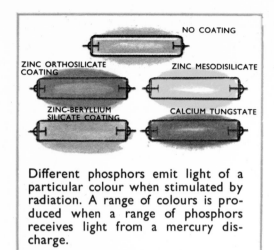

NO COATING

ZINC ORTHOSILICATE COATING

ZINC MESODISILICATE

ZINC-BERYLLIUM SILICATE COATING

CALCIUM TUNGSTATE

Different phosphors emit light of a particular colour when stimulated by radiation. A range of colours is produced when a range of phosphors receives light from a mercury discharge.

partly on the type of phosphor and partly on the frequency of the power source. That is why the colour of light given off can be changed by varying the frequency.

Uses of Phosphors

Phosphors find their biggest application in lighting and television. The newer phosphors in fluorescent strip lights have small additions of antimony and manganese in them. They produce a warm white light which does not fall off in brightness with use. Such phosphors have the advantage of being highly efficient.

Apart from their use in radar screens, and cathode ray tubes, special phosphors have been developed for colour television tubes. The need here is for three different phosphors which emit red, green, and blue colours when stimulated by an electron beam. Any colour may be created by blending these three colours.

Different phosphors keep glowing for different times after the light or electron beam is switched off. For X-ray screens, phosphors with a short after-glow are required to prevent blurring of the image to be photographed in a medical diagnosis. A suitable phosphor is calcium tungstate, which gives a deep blue light for a very short time.

For 'solid' lighting, panels are made of zinc sulphide enriched with copper. The panels can light a room, or act as a night-light, or an electric light switch can be constantly aglow so that it can be easily found in the dark. Instrument panels in a pilot's aircraft cabin are made out of such phosphor panels.

Phosphors form the coatings of scintillation counters for measuring radioactivity from isotopes.

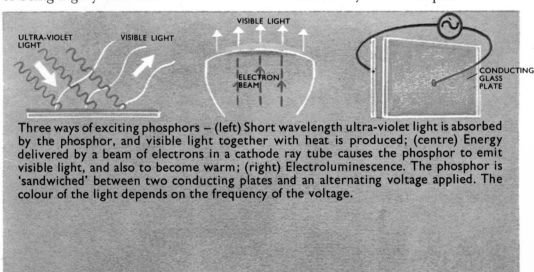

Three ways of exciting phosphors – (left) Short wavelength ultra-violet light is absorbed by the phosphor, and visible light together with heat is produced; (centre) Energy delivered by a beam of electrons in a cathode ray tube causes the phosphor to emit visible light, and also to become warm; (right) Electroluminescence. The phosphor is 'sandwiched' between two conducting plates and an alternating voltage applied. The colour of the light depends on the frequency of the voltage.

The Unseen Spectra

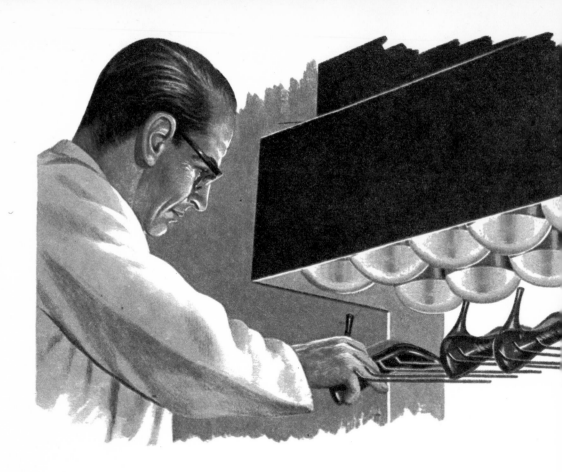

CHAPTER EIGHT

The Infra-Red

THERE are three ways of trans-
ferring heat from one place to
another: by conduction, convection,
and by radiation. Most forms of
domestic heating are based on the last
two of these. An electric bar-fire,
for instance, is principally a radiator
of heat. Because the heating element
is hot, it radiates energy in the form
of electromagnetic waves. These waves
result from movements of electrons,
and from vibrations of the atoms
and molecules which constitute the
metal in the element.

The fact that the element is glowing,
or *incandescent*, means that it is emitting some visible light. But more

important with an electric fire, the
element is giving off *infra-red* heat
radiation. This is invisible to the
human eye, but it can be detected
because it produces the sensation of
heat in any part of the human body
that it strikes.

In the electromagnetic spectrum,
infra-red rays lie between visible light
and radio waves. The wavelengths of
these radiations are longer than those
of visible light, but shorter than
radio waves. They carry less energy
than light waves: because of this
they are more difficult to detect by
photography. Only those infra-red
rays with wavelengths very close

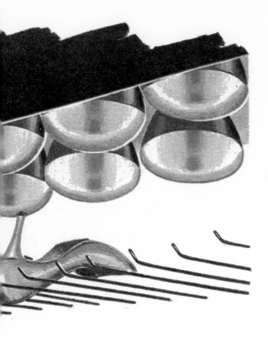

Repairing shoes with the aid of infra-red. The cement holding the worn sole to the rest of the shoe is 'activated' in an infra-red oven, and the sole can then be easily removed without damaging the upper leather.

to the visible region have enough energy to blacken a photographic film.

Infra-red radiation is produced by the vibrations of electrons, atoms and molecules. When these are agitated or excited it is propagated through space with the speed of light (30,000,000,000 cm./sec.), and heats objects in its path by causing vibrations of the electrons, atoms and molecules which make up these objects. The greater the energy of these vibrations, the shorter the wavelength of the infra-red radiation. Infra-red waves travel out in straight lines from their source, as do all electromagnetic waves. So radiant heat can be felt only by something in direct line with a source. It is similar in many ways to visible and ultra-violet rays.

In the other forms of heating, by convection and conduction, the heat can 'travel round corners'. In the case of convection the hot air itself is carried from the heater to the body receiving it. The air molecules through which the infra-red radiation passes absorb it hardly at all. The radiation travels on until it hits, and is absorbed by, a denser medium.

The major source of heat on the Earth is the infra-red radiation from the Sun. A little of this radiation is trapped or absorbed as it passes through the Earth's atmosphere. The rest heats the Earth when it strikes the ground and is absorbed.

Most forms of domestic heating are concerned with raising the overall temperature of a room, and so both convection and radiation provide a useful means of heat-transfer.

Sometimes, however, it may be required to heat one particular place. The only way of doing this efficiently

Rearing chicks under infra-red lamps. These provide gentle, draught-proof warmth, which accelerates the growth of the chicks.

is by pure radiation. Convection currents heat up other parts of the room, and may easily be disturbed by draughts.

Infra-red lamps

Convection currents can be stopped by enclosing the element in a glass bulb, thus making it into an infrared lamp. This is similar to the incandescent filament lamp which gives out visible light. To direct the infra-red radiation, part of the inside surface of the bulb is coated with a material which reflects infra-red, and helps to beam the radiation all in one direction.

The element, or filament, of an infra-red lamp is at a lower temperature than the filament of an ordinary lamp bulb (2,400°C., compared with about 3,000°C.). The filament lamp has to be at a higher temperature so that a larger proportion of its radiation is of visible light. The lower-temperature infra-red lamp gives a maximum intensity of radiation at about 15,000 Ångstrom units (the visible spectrum ends at about 7,600 Å). The filament is less hot, so the radiations are less energetic. Radiant heat travels with the speed of light, so that radiation is transferred almost instantaneously from one part of a room to another.

The speed with which any object is heated with infra-red radiation depends mainly on the difference of temperature between the colder, heat-absorbing body and the emitter of the infra-red. With infra-red lamps the difference in temperature may be about 2,000°C., so the warming-up will be rapid.

Uses of Infra-red

Infra-red radiation has a large number of applications as a source of heat. Because it is unaffected by draughts, it can be used as efficient out-of-door or indoor 'spot' heating. There are many industrial uses of infra-red lamps. They can be used for baking and drying paints, enamels and varnishes on practically all types of materials. One snag in this process is that paints will dry at different rates, depending on their colour. Black paint dries more quickly than white paint. A white paint reflects a great deal of infra-red and so absorbs heat more slowly than a black paint which absorbs practically all the radiation falling on it.

Infra-red is used as a safe and convenient provider of heat for distilling liquids, especially those which are volatile (turn to vapour easily) or highly inflammable, and which could easily be set on fire if a naked flame or a heat source open to the air were used. The hot part of an infra-red lamp is completely enclosed.

Infra-red grills cook far more quickly than ordinary grills, where heat would have to be conducted and convected through to the centre of the joint. When meat is grilled under infra-red, the radiation is able to penetrate throughout the meat. Instead of taking the longest to cook, the centre may be cooked quicker than the outside. Heat can escape from the outside, but not from the centre, so the outside would tend to become cooler.

Although its main use is in heating, infra-red has many other more specialised applications.

Car headlights enable the driver to see in the dark because they send out beams of visible light. The driver sees the light rays reflected from any object that the visible radiation strikes. Much the same thing can be done with infra-red rays, but the driver does not reveal his own position in doing so. This has many military applications, especially in target range-finders and weapon guiders. Naturally the driver's eyes would not be able to detect the reflected 'picture' of infra-red radiation. Instead he uses a device called an *infra-red image converter*. This, quite literally, converts the infra-red 'picture' into a visible picture. The radiation falls on a sensitive photo-cathode, which forms part of an apparatus similar to the cathode-ray tubes used in television sets. The radiation liberates electrons from the photo-cathode (the *photo-electric* effect), the electrons are accelerated by an electric field, and travel on to strike a fluorescent screen. There, each electron causes a spot of visible light, the intensity of the light being proportional to the intensity of the infra-red radiation striking the cathode.

A cut-away diagram of a short-wave infra-red lamp. The graph shows the range of wavelengths emitted by this sort of lamp. Most of the radiation is outside the visible region.

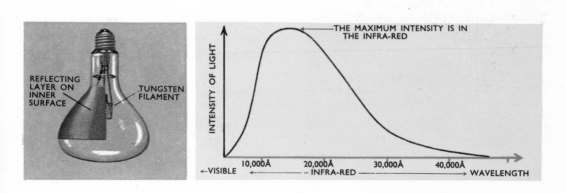

An infra-red image converter enables the soldier to see in the dark. Infra-red rays beamed in the direction of his target are reflected by the target and converted into a visible image.

CHAPTER NINE

The Ultra-Violet

STARTING at about 12 miles above the Earth's surface, and reaching its peak density at a height of about 27 miles, is a layer of the gas ozone (O_3). This ozone layer fulfils a very important function. It has the property of trapping the harmful ultra-violet rays radiated by the Sun, and preventing them from reaching the Earth.

Ultra-violet rays are electro-magnetic radiations whose wavelengths range from 120A to 3,900A (an Angstrom unit is one ten millionth of a millimetre). In the electro-magnetic spectrum they are sandwiched between visible light on the longer wavelength side and penetrating X-rays on the shorter wavelength side.

The Sun is an extremely hot body. Because its surface is at about 6,000°C it is *incandescent*—it emits a large amount of electro-magnetic radiation, most of it being of visible light. However, it emits both infra-red and ultra-violet light as well.

Visible light affects the sensitive part of the retina of the eye, and produces the sensation of light. The boundary between visible and ultra-violet light is the boundary between the seen and the unseen. While visible light is harmless, ultra-violet light may have adverse effects on living tissues. The effect it has depends on its wavelength. The ultra-violet region from 3,000A to 1,850A is known to be especially lethal, and these rays are in fact used for killing harmful bacteria in hospitals and in food warehouses, where the bacteria are killed before they have a chance to decompose the food.

Teeth and fingernails both contain fluorescent materials, which glow when illuminated by invisible ultra-violet light. (N.B. In real life special glasses would be worn to protect the eyes.)

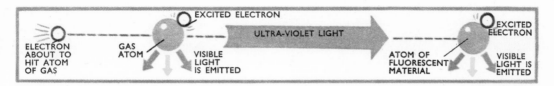

Ultra-violet light is made in a discharge tube by bombarding mercury atoms with electric current. Fluorescence converts ultra-violet light into visible light.

Longer wavelength ultra-violet rays in the region from 3,900A to 3,000A may have a beneficial effect in moderately small doses. While producing a brown pigment in the skin (suntanning), ultra-violet rays change complicated organic substances such as *ergosterol* in human skin cells, into Vitamin D. This is an important vitamin, and it can then be absorbed into the blood stream, and used.

Very little is known about the effects of the very short ultra-violet rays on living things. These are very difficult to control experimentally because neither glass nor quartz (a transparent mineral which transmits some ultra-violet rays) allow short ultra-violet rays to pass through them. This means that they cannot be focussed by 'optical' instruments, such as the ultra-violet microscope. Of all the ultra-violet rays, only those relatively beneficial to human life can penetrate the ozone barrier.

Ultra-violet light alters living tissues because it represents enough energy to bring about a chemical change. Suntanning, or the killing of bacteria, are both results of changes in the chemical structure of the materials within living cells. Usually a certain amount of energy is required for the change, and the cell is especially sensitive to the particular wavelength of ultra-violet which corresponds to this energy (the amount of energy carried by any electro-magnetic radiation depends on its wavelength).

Fluorescence

Some substances, even though they may not react chemically when exposed to ultra-violet light, absorb the radiation strongly. These are often *fluorescent* substances. They absorb the ultra-violet light, and then immediately reconvert the energy into visible light. Teeth and fingernails are fluorescent, and glow softly (*i.e.* emit visible light) when illuminated by an ultra-violet lamp. When diffe-

Ultra-violet waves have wavelengths of from 3900A *(bordering the visible spectrum) to* 120A *(bordering the X-ray region).*

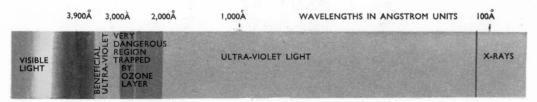

rent kinds of material fluoresce, they emit different colours of light. This leads to one method of testing paintings for authenticity. When, for instance, paint containing white lead fluoresces, it emits white light. White zinc paint, on the other hand, gives out a lemon yellow fluorescent light. The various yellow pigments used in yellow paint all give slightly different fluorescent colours, and thus by examining a painting closely with ultra-

violet light, experts can glean information about who painted it, and when it was painted.

Fluorescence occurs when the atoms in the substance are excited by the ultra-violet light. The atom tries to revert as soon as possible to its stable, unexcited state. It may re-radiate exactly the same wavelength of light it absorbed. But usually, instead of emitting one, high energy, ultra-violet wavelength, it emits two

Ultra-violet light is used to kill bacteria. Here the light from a mercury vapour discharge lamp is being used to keep air bacteria-free in a laboratory where penicillin is made.

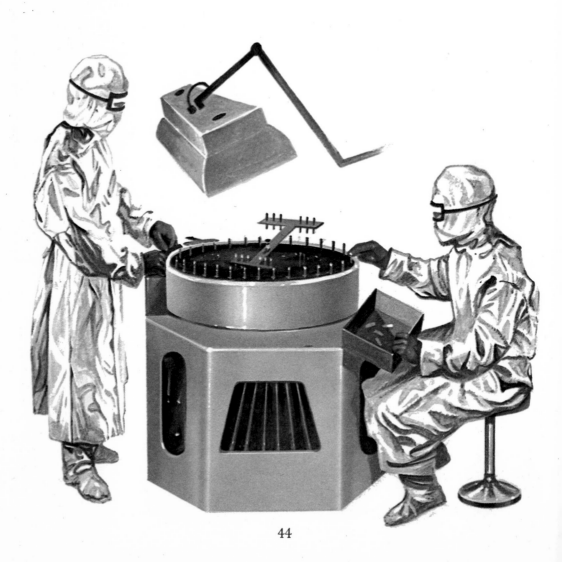

or more lower energy wavelengths, which will probably be in the visible region.

Making Ultra-violet Light

Very little ultra-violet light is received naturally by the Earth, since the ozone layer in the atmosphere blocks it so effectively. It can, however, be made very easily in gas discharge tubes. A very strong source of ultra-violet light is a *mercury vapour* discharge tube. If the mercury vapour is excited by passing an electric current through the tube it emits both visible and ultra-violet wavelengths. The radiations are produced in much the same way as in fluorescence. Instead of receiving light energy, the atoms of the gas are being given energy from the electric current (a stream of tiny negatively charged particles—electrons). When the mercury atom is de-excited, much of the excess energy is released in ultra-violet light.

Discharge tubes are used mainly for making visible light. If the inside of a mercury vapour tube is coated with a fluorescent material, practically all the ultra-violet from the discharge is converted into visible light by fluorescence. These discharge tubes are found in modern 'strip' lighting, and the fluorescent materials are chosen so that they give out a good, white light. Any unabsorbed ultra-violet is stopped by the glass tube. (Most glasses are, in fact, opaque to ultra-violet light.)

A discharge tube can be adapted to give out pure ultra-violet light by blackening the outside of the tube, thus stopping the visible radiations. The tube of this 'black' lamp must be made, not of glass, but of quartz, which transmits ultra-violet of this wavelength range easily.

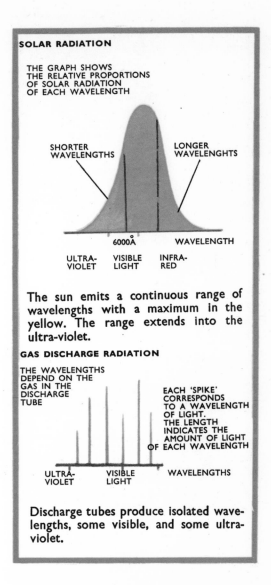

SOLAR RADIATION

THE GRAPH SHOWS THE RELATIVE PROPORTIONS OF SOLAR RADIATION OF EACH WAVELENGTH

SHORTER WAVELENGTHS

LONGER WAVELENGHTS

6000Å   WAVELENGTH

ULTRA-VIOLET   VISIBLE LIGHT   INFRA-RED

The sun emits a continuous range of wavelengths with a maximum in the yellow. The range extends into the ultra-violet.

GAS DISCHARGE RADIATION

THE WAVELENGTHS DEPEND ON THE GAS IN THE DISCHARGE TUBE

EACH 'SPIKE' CORRESPONDS TO A WAVELENGTH OF LIGHT. THE LENGTH INDICATES THE AMOUNT OF LIGHT OF EACH WAVELENGTH

ULTRA-VIOLET   VISIBLE LIGHT   WAVELENGTHS

Discharge tubes produce isolated wavelengths, some visible, and some ultra-violet.

Of course discharge tubes are not the only means of making ultra-violet light. It can be made, as in the Sun, by making something hot enough so that some of its radiation is in the ultra-violet. This is, however, an extremely inefficient method of production, since even with bodies as hot as the Sun, only a fraction of the total radiation is of ultra-violet light. The hotter the body, the larger the proportion of ultra-violet light it radiates.

X-ray Spectra

THE use of X-rays is now quite common-place. Within a few weeks of Rontgen's historic discovery, in 1895, that these invisible rays could penetrate matter and expose photographic film, they were being used to help surgeons locate and diagnose fractures.

Since that time, their practical uses have grown enormously, not only in medicine, but in industry. But to the fundamental scientist, the study of X-rays has provided valuable information about the nature of matter itself. Not only has it given him insight into the way that atoms and molecules are arranged in crystals – it has also answered many questions about the structures of atoms themselves.

How X-rays are Made

X-rays are a form of radiant energy, very similar to light and radio waves, but of much shorter wavelength. They are thrown out by an atom when the energy of an electron 'missile' is absorbed.

In an X-ray tube, electrons are emitted by a heated, negatively-charged cathode and are accelerated to bombard a positively-charged anode. The speeds attained by the electrons depend on the voltage difference between the two electrodes. If a voltage difference of 100,000 volts is applied, electrons can be accelerated to half the speed of light.

In the atom, there is a tiny, positively-charged nucleus, surrounded by a cloud of electrons. These electrons are arranged in energy shells. Electrons in the inner shells possess the lowest energies – they need to be given much more energy to be removed from the atom than those in the outer shells. Whatever shell an electron is in, it needs a definite amount of energy to remove it from the atom. When a very high energy electron is absorbed by the atom an electron in an innermost shell is displaced from the shell. This

The X-rays are split into different wavelengths by reflecting them from a flat crystal. (Left) The different X-ray spectral lines are formed on the photographic film, for different positions of the crystal. (Right) The X-ray intensity-wavelength graph is 'drawn' by measuring the intensities of the reflection at different angles using the ionization chamber.

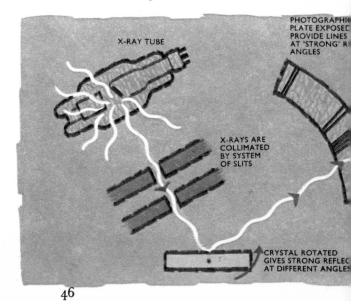

X-RAY TUBE

PHOTOGRAPHIC PLATE EXPOSED PROVIDE LINES AT 'STRONG' RI ANGLES

X-RAYS ARE COLLIMATED BY SYSTEM OF SLITS

CRYSTAL ROTATED GIVES STRONG REFLEC AT DIFFERENT ANGLE

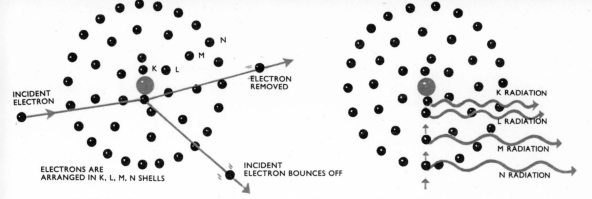

INCIDENT
ELECTRON

ELECTRON
REMOVED

N

M

K L

ELECTRONS ARE
ARRANGED IN K, L, M, N SHELLS

INCIDENT
ELECTRON BOUNCES OFF

K RADIATION

L RADIATION

M RADIATION

N RADIATION

state of affairs does not last very long, because the displaced electron is immediately replaced by a higher-energy electron that normally resides in the next shell out. Then, an electron from the *next* shell moves in to take the place of the second electron, and its place is taken by an electron from the next shell out. Each of the electrons' 'journeys' from one shell to the next makes the atom radiate energy of a definite wavelength. The transition to an inner, higher energy shell gives out (*hard*) radiation of high energy and short wavelength. Radiation caused by a replacement in an outer shell will produce longer wavelength (*soft*) X-rays.

The X-ray Spectrum

The radiations involving electrons

Producing X-rays. The target is bombarded by fast-moving electrons and an inner (K) electron is removed. An electron from the next (L) shell takes its place, and its place in turn is taken by an M electron. Similar transitions can occur in all the shells so a mixture of K, L, M, N radiation, of different wavelengths, is emitted.

in the different shells have been named according to the traditional names given to the shells. For example, radiation arising from the removal of an electron from the inner 'K' shell will result in radiation of a particular wavelength. This is called *K* radiation. Radiations from the next L, M, N, shells result in the longer wavelength L, M, N, radiations, so when a target is bombarded with electrons, a mixture of radiations is thrown out. But the

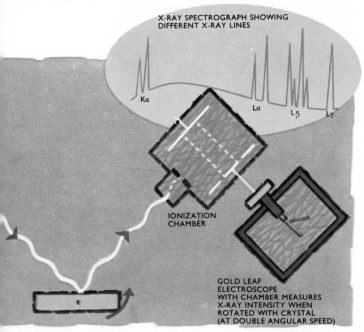

X-RAY SPECTROGRAPH SHOWING
DIFFERENT X-RAY LINES

Kα

Lα

Lβ

Lγ

IONIZATION
CHAMBER

GOLD LEAF
ELECTROSCOPE
WITH CHAMBER MEASURES
X-RAY INTENSITY WHEN
ROTATED WITH CRYSTAL
(AT DOUBLE ANGULAR SPEED)

shortest wavelength radiation that is emitted cannot have a greater energy than that of the electrons that bombard the target. Only high energy electrons can produce K radiation. Electrons of lower energy will produce a mixture of L,M,N, radiations.

Just as the light emitted by an ordinary lamp can be split up into its different wavelengths by a prism in a spectrometer, so can the X-rays in an X-ray *spectrometer*. In the *Bragg spectrometer*, the beam of X-rays is reflected from a flat crystal. In the crystal are

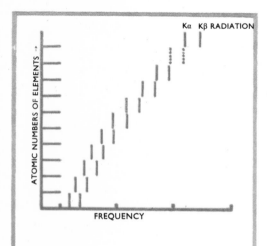

In 1913 Moseley found a simple relationship between the positive charge on the nucleus of an atom (the *atomic number*) and the frequencies of the 'K' X-rays given out by the atom.

In its simplest form it showed that the frequency of the K radiation increased in 'jumps' as shown in the diagram, going from one atom to the next in the Periodic Table. Where there was a gap in the diagram there was an undiscovered element, and new elements have been discovered, and their atomic numbers found, by studying X-ray spectra. Even more important, Moseley's work established the importance of the atomic numbers of elements – that the essential difference between one element and another was the difference in numerical positive charge on the nucleus.

layers of atoms, one after the other, and X-rays are reflected from these different layers. (Strictly speaking, this is a *diffraction* effect, rather than reflection. The waves are not reflected as by a mirror but are scattered in all directions by the atoms in the crystal planes.) The X-rays reflected from one layer 'mix' with X-rays from the next. At certain angles of reflection the X-ray 'waves' travel exactly one complete extra wavelength in passing to the second layer, and back. Then, the two sets of reflected waves are added together, because 'crest' coincides with 'crest' for a particular angle of reflection, so with X-rays of a particular wavelength, there is a strong reflection.

If the crystal is rotated in the X-ray beam, the different angles of reflection each represent 'strong' reflection angles for a different particular wavelength of X-rays. Suppose the target in an X-ray tube is giving out a mixture of radiations (K,L,M,N,). By rotating the crystal, a series of strong K,L,M,N, reflections will flash into view. The strengths of the reflected rays can either be measured using an ionization chamber or scintillation counter or can be registered on a photographic plate and then measured. By noting the variation in X-ray intensity with angle of rotation, the change in intensity with X-ray wavelength is found.

In this *X-ray spectrograph* the various radiation 'peaks', corresponding to the K,L,M,N, radiations, are clearly seen. The different 'lines' (K,L,M,N etc.) are, in fact, not single peaks but are split into a number of single peaks. This is because an electron can have a number of different energies within a shell. These give rise to a mixture of radiations. For example, there might be $K\alpha, K\beta, K\gamma$, peaks all

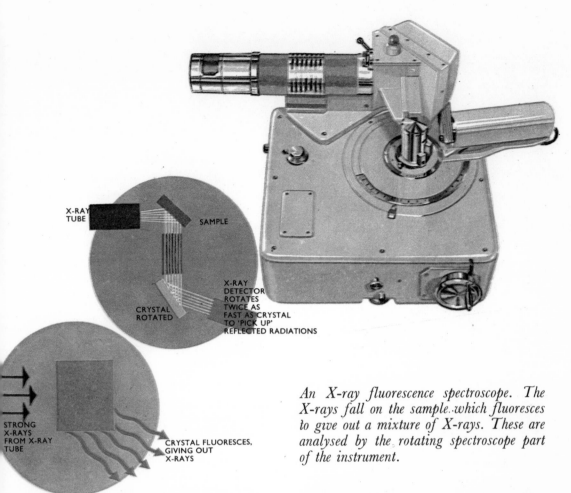

An X-ray fluorescence spectroscope. The X-rays fall on the sample which fluoresces to give out a mixture of X-rays. These are analysed by the rotating spectroscope part of the instrument.

appearing on the spectrograph, each representing an energy subdivision.

Applications of X-ray Spectroscopy

The existence of the various radiation peaks has provided valuable information to support the modern theory of the atom. In addition, the spectrograms that are obtained are always the same for atoms of a particular element, so a valuable analytical method, of great use to the chemist, is made available.

In practice, there is a particularly valuable variation of this method as an analytical tool. This is in *X-ray fluoroscopy*. It is very similar to the phenomenon of *optical fluorescence*. Atoms can be made to give out visible light if they are stimulated by light of the appropriate wavelength. Atoms also give out X-rays if they are stimulated by X-rays of the appropriate wavelength.

A very intense beam of X-rays falls on the unknown substance, from a high energy X-ray tube. The photons of different energy in the beam cause electrons in the atoms of the substance to be displaced and X-rays are emitted. The wavelengths of the X-rays are analysed using a rotating crystal spectrometer. The spectrum can be shown on a photographic film and the method provides a very quick and reliable method of analysis. The positions of the peaks on the photograph indicate what elements are present. The sizes of the peaks indicate the quantities of each element present.

CHAPTER ELEVEN

X-ray Diffraction

CRYSTALS have always fascinated Man because of the beauty of their simple geometric forms and the way many of them sparkle when light falls on them.

Long ago, Man suspected that their external symmetry must be due to the arrangements of atoms within them, but for a very long time this could be neither proved nor disproved. It was simply not possible to see the atoms inside a crystal. Ordinary light can never be used to see them, but by using X-rays, a picture of the inside of a crystal can be built up. To do this, X-rays are bounced off the layers of atoms forming the crystals.

An Atlantic roller will sweep straight on past a cork bobbing in its path and certainly will not be reflected back by the cork. In just the same way, light waves sweep past the atoms in a crystal and are not deflected from their path. The story is quite different if the rollers strike a cliff. This time they are reflected back, for the cliff is compara-

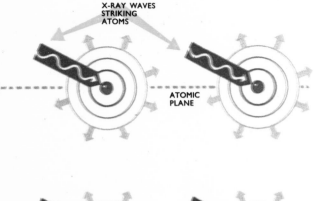

X-RAY WAVES STRIKING ATOMS

ATOMIC PLANE

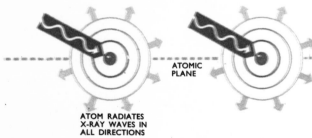

ATOMIC PLANE

ATOM RADIATES X-RAY WAVES IN ALL DIRECTIONS

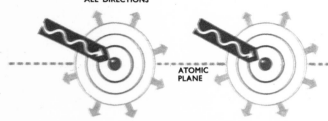

ATOMIC PLANE

ATO

Crystal illuminated by X-rays. When they are bombarded, the atoms in the crystal emit X-rays in all directions. In a particular direction, the crests and troughs coincide and reinforce each other. In other directions they tend to cancel out.

tively large. X-rays behave in a similar fashion when they meet atoms in their path. The rays are reflected by them. X-rays, then, can be used to perceive atoms.

X-rays are similar to visible light rays but of much smaller wave length. The size of a wave is of roughly the same order of size as the atom. For this reason atoms are capable of reflecting the waves.

In 1937 Sir William Bragg displayed a shadow picture of a single cell of oxalic acid and another of the molecule of a pigment called monastral blue.

The pigment 'picture' revealed four benzene rings surrounding an inner ring of nitrogen and carbon atoms and in the centre of all, an atom of nickel or copper.

The method by which these results were obtained has now become routine

in many industrial laboratories.

An X-ray tube produces a beam of X-rays by shooting a stream of electrons out of its cathode at a high voltage to strike a target in the tube. As a result, the target gives out X-rays, but X-rays of a variety of different wave length. A narrow slit, placed in the path of the beam allows only a thin 'wedge' of radiation to pass through and a purifying filter 'kills' all wave lengths except those of a particular one.

The monochromatic (one wave length only) beam falls on the crystal whose structure is being investigated. The crystal is mounted on a turntable which can be rotated by a fine screw.

The tiny waves hitting the atoms which form the crystal are reflected off the inclined surface and pass down a tube into an *ionization chamber* fitted with a narrow window through which X-rays can easily pass. The rays pour through this window knocking the air molecules in their path to pieces. The air becomes *ionized* and is capable of conducting an electric current.

The outside of the metal chamber is connected to one terminal of a high-tension battery while the other terminal is connected to the outer casing of a gold leaf electroscope which in turn has its gold leaf connected to an electrode placed inside the chamber and insulated from the walls by a rubber or ebonite cork.

When a beam of X-rays passes through the chamber, the current leaks from the walls to the plate. The difference of potential between the gold leaves and the casing of the chamber falls and the leaves collapse as some charge is lost. When no X-ray beam is passing, the air no longer conducts and the gold leaves remain separate. Therefore the rate of collapse is an

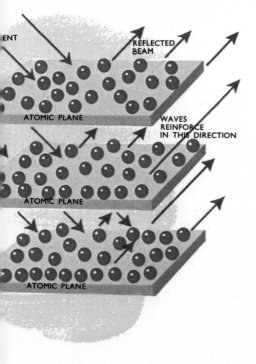

ENT

REFLECTED BEAM

ATOMIC PLANE

WAVES REINFORCE IN THIS DIRECTION

ATOMIC PLANE

ATOMIC PLANE

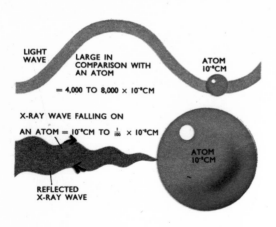

LIGHT WAVE

LARGE IN COMPARISON WITH AN ATOM

= 4,000 TO 8,000 × 10⁻⁸CM

ATOM 10⁻⁸CM

X-RAY WAVE FALLING ON

AN ATOM = 10⁻⁸CM TO 1/100 × 10⁻⁸CM

ATOM 10⁻⁸CM

REFLECTED X-RAY WAVE

An atom is too small to reflect an ordinary light wave, but is large enough to reflect an X-ray.

indication of intensity of the X-ray beam – quick collapse, high intensity of X-rays.

In 1912, Bragg discovered an extraordinary phenomenon. He found that as the crystal was slowly rotated, the intensity of the beam suddenly jumped at a certain angle and then fell away, only to jump again later.

When a crystal of aluminium oxide was rotated by Bragg, intense radiation flashed out at angles of 1°45′, 3°30′, 5°20′, 6° and 8°50′ (these were the angles between the incident radiation and the surface). Bragg rightly guessed that the reflection was due to successive planes of atoms within the crystal.

At certain angles, a glass window will reflect sunlight, flashing it back

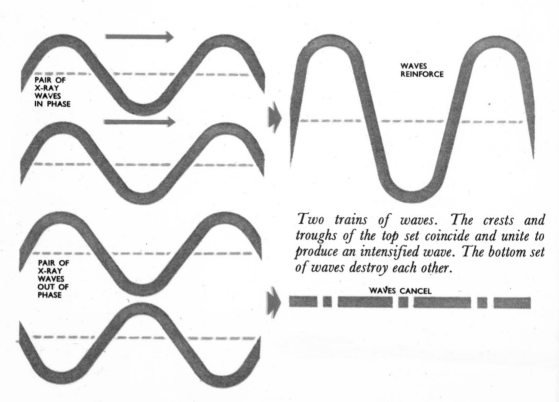

PAIR OF X-RAY WAVES IN PHASE

WAVES REINFORCE

PAIR OF X-RAY WAVES OUT OF PHASE

WAVES CANCEL

Two trains of waves. The crests and troughs of the top set coincide and unite to produce an intensified wave. The bottom set of waves destroy each other.

52

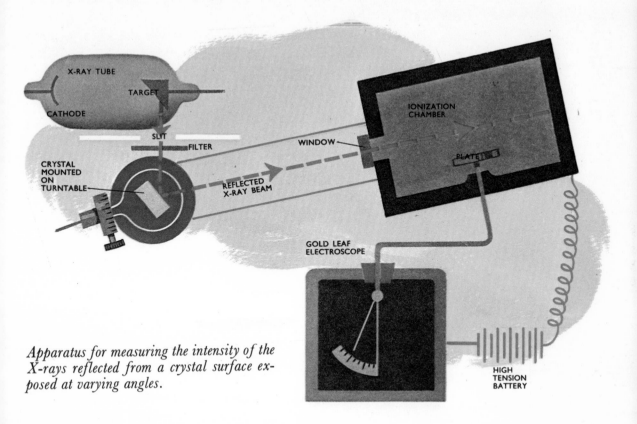

Labels within figure:
X-RAY TUBE
TARGET
CATHODE
SLIT
FILTER
CRYSTAL MOUNTED ON TURNTABLE
REFLECTED X-RAY BEAM
IONIZATION CHAMBER
WINDOW
PLATE
GOLD LEAF ELECTROSCOPE
HIGH TENSION BATTERY

Apparatus for measuring the intensity of the X-rays reflected from a crystal surface exposed at varying angles.

into the eyes of the observer. When the angle of the glass sheet is altered just a little, however, the effect vanishes. Something similar is happening with the successive reflections of X-rays, but here it is reflection from atomic planes – sheets of atoms inside the crystal.

The atoms are large objects and a great distance apart compared with the X-rays falling on them. Many of the X-rays pass between the atoms but some are reflected by them. When an atom is struck, it becomes the centre of disturbance and begins to radiate X-ray waves in all directions. An atom on the surface will be doing this; so will an atom in the plane below. The two sets of waves spreading out from each atom will interfere with each other. Where the crests of waves from both atoms coincide they will reinforce each other, but if, on the other hand, a crest of one coincides with a trough of the other then the rays mutually destroy each other and the intensity drops to zero.

The waves will reinforce each other if a wave from the lower atom is exactly one wave length behind; i.e. there is a *phase difference* of 1 wave length. The waves will also reinforce for phase differences of 2, 3, 4 wave lengths etc. They will destroy each other if the phase difference is half a wave length or $1\frac{1}{2}$ wave lengths and so on.

If millions of waves from different

53

atomic planes reinforce each other, then there will be a reflected X-ray wave of great intensity, but this maximum intensity is possible only for certain angles of incidence of the beam.

Bragg applied geometrical reasoning to the problem and produced a mathematical formula relating the wave length of the X-rays to the distance between the atomic planes and the glancing angle at which the X-ray strikes the crystal to give a reflection where the rays from different atomic planes reinforce each other.

The mathematical expression is known as *Bragg's law* and can be used to calculate the distances between atomic planes. The crystal can be 'viewed' from different sides to build up a three-dimensional picture of the atomic structure.

Metals can be studied using X-rays to find how their atomic arrangement responds when they are subjected to outside strain, heat, prolonged vibration, etc., and in fact X-rays are used to investigate the new alloys constantly being produced, because their physical properties depend very much on the internal arrangement of the atoms.

Man-made Waves

CHAPTER TWELVE

Radio Waves

RADIO waves are sent out when bursts of electric current pass along a transmitting aerial. The waves are in the form of *electromagnetic* radiation because they are created as a result of the magnetic and electric fields set up when the current flows in the aerial.

The aerial forms part of the output circuit of the transmitter, and in this circuit electrical oscillations are generated. This means that electric currents pass to and fro in the circuit a constant number of times each second. The number of oscillations each second is called the *frequency*, and each complete to and fro motion is called a *cycle*. So, if the current passes to and fro 50 times a second the frequency of the oscillation is 50 cycles per second (50 c/s).

The electrical oscillations fed to the aerial cause the electric and magnetic fields around the aerial to swell up and die away with the same frequency as the oscillations. The radiation from the aerial consists of a series of peaks and troughs of electromagnetic energy emitted at that frequency.

All electromagnetic waves travel at the speed of light (which is itself a form of electromagnetic wave motion) i.e. 3×10^{10} centimetres per second. An aerial transmitting radio waves of frequency, say, 10,000 c/s is producing 10,000 (10^4) waves every second. These would occupy 3×10^{10} centimetres if placed end to end so the length of each wave (*the wave length*) is

$$\frac{3 \times 10^{10}}{10^4} = 3 \times 10^6 \text{ centimetres or } 30,000 \text{ metres.}$$

All electromagnetic waves (radio or light waves) can be described either by their wavelengths or by their frequencies. The wavelength can automatically be found from the frequency, and vice versa. Radio waves are often specified by their wavelengths.

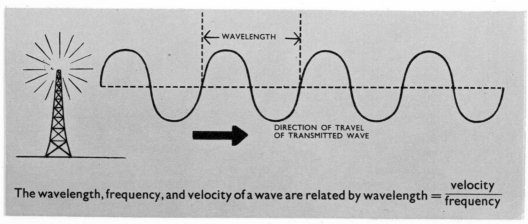

WAVELENGTH

DIRECTION OF TRAVEL OF TRANSMITTED WAVE

The wavelength, frequency, and velocity of a wave are related by wavelength $= \dfrac{\text{velocity}}{\text{frequency}}$

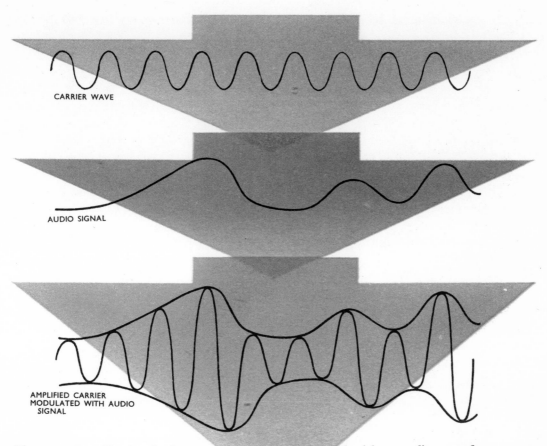

CARRIER WAVE

AUDIO SIGNAL

AMPLIFIED CARRIER
MODULATED WITH AUDIO
SIGNAL

To transmit audio signals the carrier wave is modulated with an audio wave form.

When a radio wave of a certain wavelength is transmitted from an aerial it can be picked up by the receiving aerial where it is reconverted into electric currents which alternate at the transmission frequency.

If the aerial is receiving several waves of different wavelength simultaneously the receiving circuit can be 'tuned' to select just one wavelength for amplification. This is what happens in an ordinary radio set. The aerial is receiving many hundreds of radio signals transmitted from stations all over the world, but only one is selected at the receiver, by 'tuning in' on a single wavelength.

If, however, the signal received were a single 'pure' wavelength of radio frequency, the received signal would be completely inaudible. The frequencies are far too high for the human ear to detect. In addition, to transmit information (e.g. speech or music) the wave has to be *modulated*.

The human ear can identify sound waves of frequency 20–12,000 c/s, and ordinary sounds consist of a mixture of waves of frequencies in this range. A radio wave must therefore be able to carry information which is a mixture of signals of these frequencies. In an *amplitude modulated* wave a signal is transmitted at a given frequency (the carrier frequency), but the waves are altered in *amplitude* (size) by the information the wave has to carry. For example, a normal long wave transmission is transmitted at 200,000 c/s. The radio waves are transmitted at this frequency but the sizes of the waves are being continuously altered to carry the information being broadcast.

The receiver is tuned to 200,000 c/s (1,500 metres) so it is able to receive and amplify the signal. When the signal passes through a *detector* stage the information contained in the wave modulation is extracted for further amplification.

Suppose the 200,000 c/s is being modulated at a frequency of 1,000 cycles per second. Although the transmitted wave is a pure 200,000 c/s wave, it acts as if it is a mixture of *three* waves of frequency 200,000 c/s, 200,000 − 1,000 = 199,000 c/s, and 200,000 + 1,000 = 201,000 c/s. This can be proved mathematically. A modulated wave has then a main *carrier* of frequency 200,000 c/s and two *sidebands* of frequency 201,000 c/s and 199,000 c/s. It therefore 'occupies' a frequency *band*, 2,000 cycles 'wide' from 199,000 c/s to 201,000 c/s. This is of great importance when it comes to allocating wavelengths to different broadcasting stations. If one station wishes to broadcast speech at a carrier

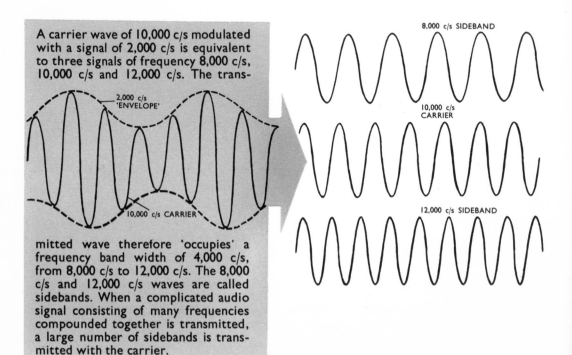

A carrier wave of 10,000 c/s modulated with a signal of 2,000 c/s is equivalent to three signals of frequency 8,000 c/s, 10,000 c/s and 12,000 c/s. The trans-

2,000 c/s 'ENVELOPE'

10,000 c/s CARRIER

8,000 c/s SIDEBAND

10,000 c/s CARRIER

12,000 c/s SIDEBAND

mitted wave therefore 'occupies' a frequency band width of 4,000 c/s, from 8,000 c/s to 12,000 c/s. The 8,000 c/s and 12,000 c/s waves are called sidebands. When a complicated audio signal consisting of many frequencies compounded together is transmitted, a large number of sidebands is transmitted with the carrier.

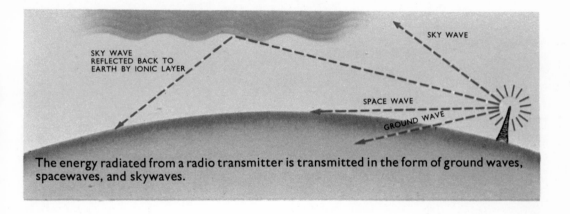

The energy radiated from a radio transmitter is transmitted in the form of ground waves, spacewaves, and skywaves.

frequency of 200,000 cycles per second, then another station broadcasting at 198,000 cycles per second will overlap the first station's 'band' because the frequencies of the side bands due to transmission of speech or music will be well into the first station's bandwidth. For this reason, each station, by international agreement, keeps not only to its own carrier frequency, but to a limited *bandwidth* as well.

The large number of radio stations thus occupy the 'air', each restricting its transmission to within a narrow range of frequencies.

Broadcast transmissions are normally transmitted in one of three *wavebands* each of which covers a range of wavelengths. A large number of stations transmit at wavelengths within each waveband. Transmissions over small and intermediate distances are normally made on the *long* and *medium* wavebands. Long waveband broadcasts are usually made at radio wavelengths greater than 1,000 metres, and medium ones in the wavelength range 700 to 1,000 metres. Transmissions over larger distances are made on the *short* waveband, of wavelength 50 metres or less.

These divisions are made because of the behaviour of the waves transmitted from an aerial at different wavelengths. The radio waves normally spread out in all directions. Those which pass along the ground are called *ground waves*. The *space waves* hit the ground at a point somewhere between the aerial and the horizon. *Sky waves* are directed towards the sky, to miss the horizon.

It so happens that most of the energy in a longer wavelength transmission is radiated in the ground wave. This means that most of the energy dies away before the waves have travelled very far. For this reason, long wavelength transmissions are used for short distances only. The same applies, to a lesser extent, to the medium waves which are also used for transmissions over distances of up to 200 miles from the transmitter.

At shorter wavelengths a strong skywave transmission is obtained. At these wavelengths the ionic layers surrounding the earth possess the property of reflecting back the radiowaves. These layers are used for sending short wave transmissions over great distances, by reflecting the skywaves back to earth at great distances from the transmitter.

CHAPTER THIRTEEN

Electromagnetism and the Velocity of Light

ELECTRICAL charges lead a double existence. When they are stationary, in *electrostatics*, each charge exerts a powerful force on another neighbouring stationary charge. In *current electricity* the moving charges usually appear in droves, but, charge for charge, they exert far smaller forces on neighbouring moving charges. So electricity grew up in two vaguely related, but seemingly separate branches. Each developed its own set of units, the *electrostatic* units (*e.s.u.*) and the *electromagnetic* units (*e.m.u.*).

Both sets of units are defined in a similar way. To relate them to quantities which can be measured in other branches of physics, they are defined by the forces charges or poles exert on each other.

Two tiny spheres are similarly charged, and one centimetre apart. If they repel each other with a force of one dyne (just over a thousandth of the pull exerted on a mass of one gram by the Earth's gravity at its surface), then each sphere is carrying one e.s.u. of charge.

Two wires carry current in the same direction, and are one centimetre apart. Because they set up a magnetic field, they exert equal and opposite forces on each other. The current flowing when the force between the wires is one dyne is used to define the e.m.u. system of units, but here there are complications. The length of the wires matter, and so do the rates of

The Dielectric Constant

The Magnetic Permeability

The force acting between the charged plates is reduced by inserting a slab of dielectric material (an electrical insulator) in between them. The dielectric constant of air in the e.s.u. scale is 1. A slab of iron increases the effect two neighbouring current-carrying wires have on each other. Iron has a higher magnetic permeability than air. Force is proportional to permeability. Because force depends on one-over-ε in one equation and μ in the other, the quantity $\dfrac{1}{\sqrt{\varepsilon\mu}}$ appears in the dimensional equation.

flow of the charges. If the lengths of the wires are each one centimetre, then the rate of flow is one e.m.u. of charge per second.

It is possible to write down equations for the force, in dynes, in either e.s. or e.m. units.

Force (in dynes) =
$$\frac{\text{first charge} \times \text{second charge (e.s.)}}{[\text{distance between charges (in cm.)}]^2}$$

and

Force (in dynes) ÷ length of wire =
$$2 \times \frac{\text{first charge (e.m.)/sec.cm.} \times \text{second charge/sec.cm.}}{[\text{distance between charges (cm.)}]}$$

When both sides of the second equation are multiplied by length, a force appears on both left-hand sides, so both right-hand sides must have identical *dimensions*, the dimensions of *force*. This is obviously impossible as the equations now stand, because the e.m.u. equation has an extra $[\text{length}]^2$ on the top and an extra $[\text{time}]^2$ on the bottom. Something is wrong with the equations,

The Velocity of Light

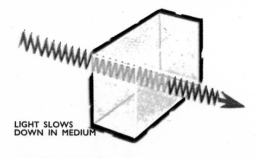

LIGHT SLOWS
DOWN IN MEDIUM

A consequence of the Electromagnetic Theory is that all electromagnetic waves (including radio waves and light waves) should travel through a substance with velocity $\sqrt{\frac{1}{\mu\varepsilon}}$. The passage of an electromagnetic wave depends on the *dielectric constant*, and on the *magnetic permeability*.

because they do not agree with each other *dimensionally*. Although the e.m.u. of charge is very much larger than the e.s.u. of charge, they are both charges, and must therefore have identical dimensions.

This discrepancy was a considerable stumbling-block, until it was found that the magic number 3×10^{10} (30,000,000,000) was the ratio of the values of e.m.u. and e.s.u. units of charge. 3×10^{10} is the velocity of light, in centimetres per second.

What is more
$$\text{velocity} = \frac{\text{length}}{\text{time}}$$
is the extent of the discrepancy between the *dimensions* of an e.m.u. and the *dimensions* of an e.s.u. So, e.m.u.'s and e.s.u.'s are related in size and dimension by a factor equal to the velocity of light.

This might seem rather a strange result, but in the late 19th century, Sir Arthur Rücker resolved the difficulty when he showed that one quantity had been missing from each of the 'force' equations. The *dielectric constant*, ε, (practically 1 for air in e.s.u. but very high, for example, for water) had been missing from the electrostatic equation, and the *magnetic permeability*, μ, (also practically 1 for air in e.m.u. but very high for materials like iron) had been missing from the electromagnetic equation. When these were written in, it was found that the dimensions in the equations were put right provided the quantity $\sqrt{\frac{1}{\mu\varepsilon}}$ had the dimensions of a velocity. This ties up well with the *electromagnetic theory* of light. One of the consequences of this theory is that electromagnetic waves – like light waves, should travel through a substance with a velocity of 3×10^{10} cm./sec.

CHAPTER FOURTEEN

Aerials — Resistance to Radiation

TRANSMITTING aerials are similar in principle to receiving aerials. They are based on the *half-wave dipole*, a piece of conducting metal of length half the wave-length of the transmitted signal. The dipole is divided at its mid-point into two parts. One electrical lead goes to each part.

The signal is in the form of to-and-fro surges of current (*alternating current*). The surges can be transferred around the circuit, from one half of the dipole, through its connecting lead, and along the other lead to the other half of the dipole. The gap in the middle of the dipole, which would stop any flow of direct, one-way current, does not prevent the alternating surges from flowing, to-and-fro, along the halves of the aerial.

But, as in all alternating current circuits, the *timing* of the current surges must be right for the maximum amount of current to flow to-and-fro. Part of a surge flowing back down an aerial can easily cancel out the following part of the surge flowing up the aerial. However, when the dipole halves are quarter of a wavelength long, the timing is right. The circuit is said to be *tuned*. Surges up and down the aerial reinforce each other at all points. The current flowing in the aerial is a maximum.

The signal can then travel to an aerial just as easily as if a 73 ohms resistance were at the end instead of the dipole aerial. 73 ohms is the *radiation resistance*, and it is virtually the same for all half-wave dipoles.

If a 73 ohms resistance were connected in place of the dipole aerial, it would *dissipate the same amount of power*

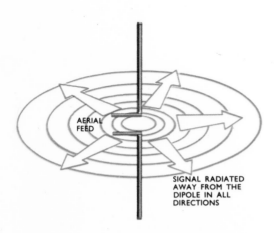

The radiation resistance is a measure of the power which can be transmitted away from a half-wave dipole, working at its resonant frequency.

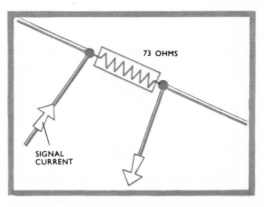

An alternating signal of the current frequency does not notice the gap at the centre of the dipole, or the termination of the circuit. It travels along the wire just as if a 73 ohm resistance were there in place of the gap.

as the aerial radiates into space. The radiation resistance is an *equivalent* resistance – it is not a real, physical resistance – and it can be calculated from the power radiated away from the aerial, and the current at the centre of the aerial.

Whenever currents change in circuits, part of the energy of the electric current is radiated away as *electromagnetic radiation*. An unchanging direct current does not radiate. Some *acceleration* in the current is necessary for this to happen.

Currents are accelerating in the two leads to the transmitting aerial, but these do not radiate either. The reason is that the two leads are parallel to each other. Both tend to radiate, but the radiations are equal and opposite, and cancel each other out. Two kinds of leads are commonly used for aerials. In one, the two leads are spaced apart from each other and parallel. The other common form is a *coaxial cable*. Here, one lead surrounds the other, preventing the lead picking up unwanted signals from outside.

The coaxial cable joined to a dipole aerial is equivalent to a resistance of around 73 ohms. This is called its *characteristic impedance*. Coaxial cables could be made with a variety of characteristic impedances, but 73 ohms is used with a dipole aerial because it 'matches' the radiation resistance of the aerial. This is the condition for the maximum transfer of power along the circuit.

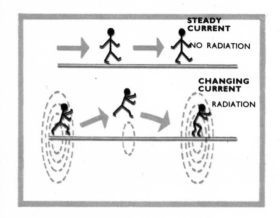

Steady currents radiate none of their energy, but whenever currents change, some energy is radiated. Parallel wires leading to the aerial tend to radiate, but the radiations cancel out.

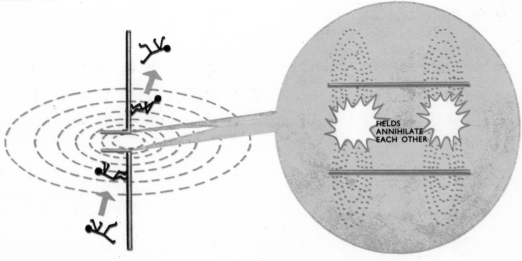

CHAPTER FIFTEEN

The Ruby Laser

A ruby is red because impurities in the crystal absorb green, yellow and ultra-violet light. When the crystal is viewed under ordinary 'white' light only the red and blue parts are transmitted through it. These rays, on striking the retina of the eye, give the ruby its overall red appearance.

The ruby removes the green and yellow parts from white light. What does it do with them? In fact it can be made to convert this light into a powerful red beam, intense enough to vaporize metals, and strong enough to carry messages across millions of miles of space. The specially made ruby capable of doing this is called a *laser*, or *light maser*.

Maser stands for 'microwave amplification by stimulated emission of radiation'. Microwaves are the waves whose wavelengths lie between those of radio waves and infra-red waves.

A laser is a maser which gives out light of shorter wavelength than microwaves, and which comes within the visible part of the spectrum.

The ruby laser is a specially manufactured ruby crystal, redder than natural rubies, and made into a cylinder. Wrapped around it is a coiled, fluorescent flash tube. This produces the light which is to operate the laser, and make it eventually emit radiation.

Many substances are stimulated by radiation, and respond by emitting a different kind of radiation. In fluorescent paints, for instance, atoms in the paint absorb ultraviolet light, and turn it into visible light. This light makes fluorescent substances appear to glow, even in the dark.

Ultra-violet light strikes certain atoms in the paint. It *excites* them, giving electrons more energy than

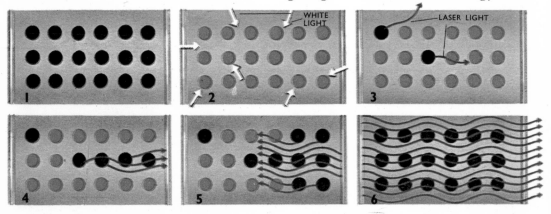

(1) *The atoms in the ruby crystal are normally unexcited (black). (2) They become excited (red) when they absorb light from the fluorescent tube, and they stay in an excited (metastable) state. (3) One or two become de-excited. If the ray is emitted parallel to the long axis of the laser, it has a good chance of hitting other atoms, and making them emit, in the same direction, light waves which are all exactly in step. (4), (5) and (6) The light bounces to and fro through the crystal, until it breaks out of one end.*

Laser Waves and Radio Waves

Radio waves are very similar to light waves, though radio wavelengths are far longer than light wavelengths. Radio waves are used to carry information – radio broadcasts, or television signals. The information is carried as a distortion of the shape of the radio wave.

Because the signal is a distortion the carrying waves must not itself be distorted in any way. The receiving set would not be able to distinguish between the wanted and unwanted distortions, and would convert both into 'noise'.

Since light waves are so similar to radio waves, there is no reason why they, too, should not be used to carry signals. In fact, in certain applications, it is thought that light waves would be superior to radio waves.

Ordinary sources of light – incandescent light bulbs, or even gas discharge lamps – are, however, wholly unsuitable. They do not give out the streams of light of precise wavelengths needed for communication purposes. This is, however, just the sort of light which the laser can produce. Speech has actually been transmitted by lasers.

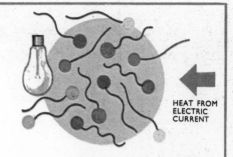

In an incandescent light bulb, light is produced by heating the filament white-hot. Electrons in the filament are excited and give out light. One electron affects another, and the light is a jumbled mixture of wavelengths.

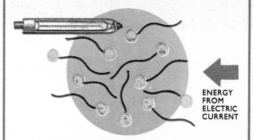

In a discharge tube, light is produced by exciting the gas atoms with an electric current. Light emission is a random affair. Pure chance decides when one gas atom should be excited, and then again, at what instant it should de-excite itself and emit a little pulse of light.

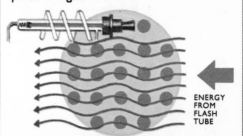

In a ruby laser the electrons around the impurity atoms are first put into an excited state by the light from the flash lamp. They drop back a little way into a *metastable state*. Then, when just one atom de-excites itself, it stimulates others to de-excite in turn. All the waves from all the stimulated atoms are exactly in step.

they would normally have. Unable to remain in this highly unstable state, the electron jumps back almost immediately to its normal state. It emits its extra energy in the form of a light wave, which is usually of a longer wavelength than the light originally exciting it.

A ruby laser operates in a similar way. But there is a very great difference between the behaviour of the impurity atoms in the ruby (these are the atoms which do all the work) and fluorescent atoms in paint. Instead of becoming de-excited almost immediately, electrons around the ruby impurity atoms drop back only part of the way. There they remain in what is called a *metastable* state – not com-

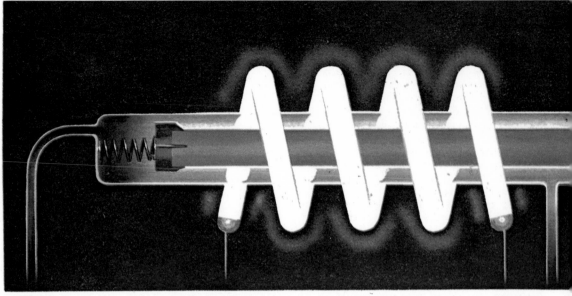

The ruby laser sends out a powerful parallel pulse of red light. The fluorescent flash tube coiled around it feeds it with light energy. The ruby laser absorbs this energy and then waits until one of its atoms suddenly releases its energy. This is the signal for all the rest of the atoms to emit light in unison.

pletely stable, but stable enough to stay in this state for a relatively long period of time.

The flash lamp wrapped around the ruby laser is turned on, and it sends a bright beam of visible light into the laser. Impurity atoms are excited by the light, and then their electrons drop into the metastable state.

Suddenly one of the atoms drops into the stable state. It may send a ray of red light out in any direction. The laser is a long ruby cylinder, and light passing out through its long sides is lost. But one ray emitted parallel to the axis of the cylinder travels through the ruby, and hits another atom. The light is of exactly the right wavelength to *stimulate* the impurity atoms (which are still metastable), make them fall back into the unexcited, normal state, and emit exactly the same wavelength of light at exactly the same instant. A doubled light beam comes from the first atom the original beam hits. The

doubled beam hits another metastable atom, is trebled in strength, hits another, and another, each time getting stronger as it gathers the energy from the metastable atoms.

The original beam of light stimulates metastable atoms, and is *amplified* as a result. It hits one of the ends of the cylinder (which are both silvered to make them behave like mirrors), is reflected back into the crystal, hits more atoms, grows in strength, and is reflected from the other end. The beam bounces back between the ends of the laser, each time becoming stronger. Finally the beam is strong enough to pass right through the end of the laser (which is not silvered so much as the other end).

The wavelength of the light is very precise (actually this kind of laser gives out *two* very precise wavelengths, one of 7,009 Å and the other of 7,014 Å. An Ångstrom unit is one ten-millionth of a millimetre). The

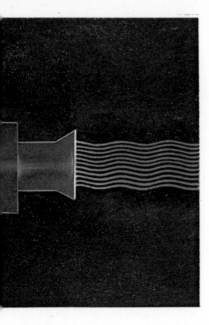

light has been amplified by bouncing to and fro, parallel to the long axis of the crystal, so the beam is parallel to within a twentieth of a degree. It does not spread out much as it travels, but remains a concentrated, parallel beam of light. It is estimated that laser light beamed at the moon could be made to spread out so little that, even after travelling two hundred and fifty thousand miles through space it would make a spot of light only two miles in diameter on the moon.

Advantages of Laser Light

Laser light is very different from the light given out by an ordinary incandescent electric light bulb. Laser light contains one or more precise wavelengths. Incandescent 'white' light is a jumbled mixture of light waves of all wavelengths. The waves are not all of the same length, so even if the crest of one wave starts out with the crest of another (and so reinforces the total effect of the light rays) it does not do so for long. The waves soon get out of step, and partially cancel each other. The effectiveness of the light is reduced.

In addition, all the waves given out by all the atoms in a laser are in step. One wave stimulates another wave, and, because the stimulated wave is emitted *immediately*, the waves are absolutely in step. Atoms excited after being heated by the electric current supplied to a light bulb, may give out light at any time. It is a completely random affair. There is no knowing at what instant an atom will emit light, and so the crests of its waves will rarely coincide with the crests of other waves.

An incandescent light bulb gives out light in all directions. But in the laser, only light parallel to the long axis of the crystal can be transmitted and amplified.

History of Lasers and Masers

The first maser was made in 1954. It was very different from the ruby laser. Ammonia molecules were used instead of the ruby. This maser was a true maser, since it gave out microwaves (i.e. waves of longer wavelength than the ruby laser). Energy was supplied to the maser not through a fluorescent flash tube (as in the laser), but by an electromagnetic field oscillating at a microwave frequency.

Since then, many kinds of substances have been tried out as lasers and masers. These range from gases to semi-conductor diodes. They are still very much in the development stage.

Many uses for lasers and masers have been suggested. Apart from carrying radio and television broadcasts, the intense laser beam may be used for welding metals, killing abnormal living tissues, or causing chemical reactions.

CHAPTER SIXTEEN

Television by Laser

AS more and more different radio and television programmes are broadcast, the 'space' for them in the air becomes more and more crowded. For the programmes are carried between transmitting station and receiving station on radio waves, or kinds of electrical and magnetic disturbances which travel with the speed of light. Different programmes are carried on waves of different frequencies for the simple reason that it is possible to design electric circuits which pick out signals of one frequency only. In this way, one programme can be singled out from all the rest transmitted.

But if there was one signal broadcast on a wave of frequency 200,000 cycles per second, and another on a wave of frequency 200,001 cycles per second, then the radio set would not be able to distinguish one from the other. Each programme, in fact, occupies not just one radio frequency,

cycles per second wide. A television programme broadcast on a radio wave of 60,000,000 cycles per second might occupy about all the 'space' in the frequency band from 59,500,000 cycles per second to 60,500,000 cycles per second. This band is called a *channel*. (These radio waves are said to be of V.H.F., or Very High Frequency, and the usual unit for them is the Megacycle – one million cycles). Future television broadcasts will have to occupy still higher and higher frequency bands, stretching into the ultra-high-frequency (U.H.F.) region, then into the microwave region. At these very high frequencies, entirely

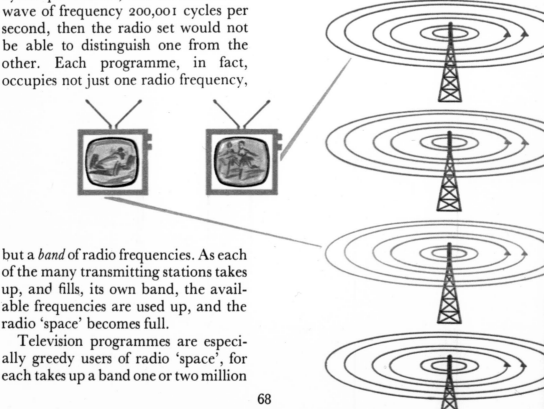

but a *band* of radio frequencies. As each of the many transmitting stations takes up, and fills, its own band, the available frequencies are used up, and the radio 'space' becomes full.

Television programmes are especially greedy users of radio 'space', for each takes up a band one or two million

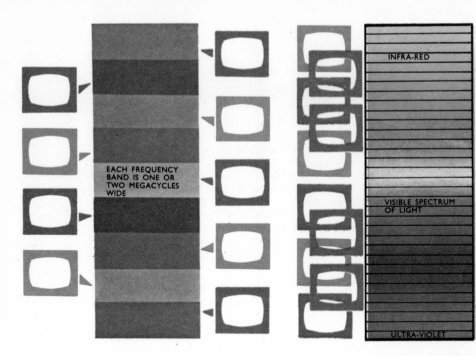

Each different programme takes up a large amount of radio 'space'.

Light waves offer 'space' for far more television channels. It has been estimated that there is 'space' for 80 million of them.

new transmitting and receiving equipment is needed.

In spite of this, there is one great advantage of using high frequencies. There is more 'room' in them. While

As more different programmes are broadcast, the available bands of frequencies are rapidly filled.

the radio 'space' between 1 and 10 megacycles can accommodate nine 1-megacycle wide television programmes, the 'space' between 100 and 1,000 megacycles per second can

accommodate about 900, and the space between 10,000 and 100,000, about 90,000.

Waves of this kind of frequency are called *microwaves*. Although they represent a great deal of available 'space' they are more difficult to produce and receive than radio waves of lower frequency. It seems likely that microwaves will be jumped over entirely, as a new method has been found of making waves of even higher frequency.

The new method, the *laser* method, makes available frequencies of up to a *thousand million* megacycles. So it could accommodate up to 900 million separate television programmes. Leaving a bit of 'space' around each one, it is thought practicable for the laser beams to carry 80 million television channels!

Although the method for making them in a form suitable for television transmissions is new, these waves are

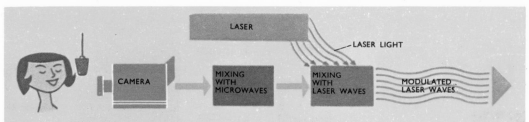

Putting the picture on to a Laser beam.

At the sending end, the signal must be superimposed on the laser light beam. The signal part is in the form of electrical oscillations. It is not thought possible to put a laser signal and an electrical oscillation together, and get them to mix directly.

The signal may first be mixed with *microwaves*, and then the mixture of audio frequencies and microwave frequencies mixed with the laser light.

very familiar. For they are *light* waves. Normally, light waves are referred to by their *wavelengths*. Their frequencies can be found by dividing their velocity by the wavelength, and, as light waves travel at the speed of light (186,000 miles per second), the frequency works out at between 100 million and a 1,000 million megacycles per second.

Light waves offer a great many advantages as means of communication, as it is virtually impossible to fill the available 'space' of them. But ordinary light is of no use. The light produced by an ordinary electric light bulb is a jumbled-up mixture of wavelengths. If it were to be used as a carrier of a television programme, then the programme would modulate, or slightly distort the signal. And if the signal is already highly distorted because it is a jumbled-up mixture of wavelengths, then the programme would be completely lost in the mix-up.

Many lasers emit light only in sudden pulses, and so are no good for transmitting television pictures. But the gas laser, which contains a mixture of helium and neon, can be made to emit laser light continuously.

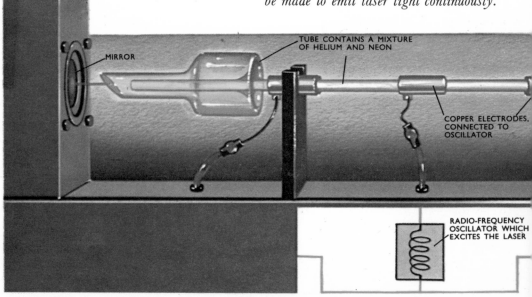

70

Taking the picture off the Laser beam.

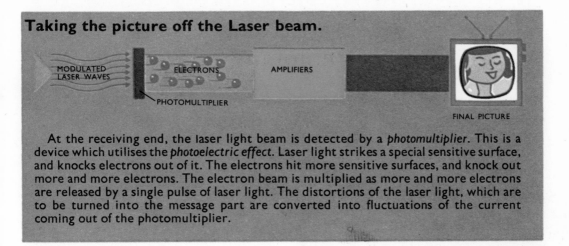

MODULATED LASER WAVES

ELECTRONS

AMPLIFIERS

PHOTOMULTIPLIER

FINAL PICTURE

At the receiving end, the laser light beam is detected by a *photomultiplier*. This is a device which utilises the *photoelectric effect*. Laser light strikes a special sensitive surface, and knocks electrons out of it. The electrons hit more sensitive surfaces, and knock out more and more electrons. The electron beam is multiplied as more and more electrons are released by a single pulse of laser light. The distortions of the laser light, which are to be turned into the message part are converted into fluctuations of the current coming out of the photomultiplier.

What is needed is a one-wavelength, or one-frequency, source of light, where the waves are sent out in continuous trains.

Such a wave is the kind emitted by a *laser*. Laser is a word coined from the initial letters of 'Light Amplification by Stimulated Emission of Radiation'. Basically this means that the laser is given some energy of assorted, mixed-up wavelengths (usually from a radio-frequency coil or a fluorescent flash tube), and it re-emits the energy as light energy with waves all of exactly the same wavelength. Some lasers have been devised so that they emit the light continuously. These are the main properties vital for an information-carrying beam of light.

Of course, it is of no use trying to deal with the light waves with the same kind of electronic circuitry used for radio waves. Entirely new apparatus must be devised to superimpose on the light wave the distortion which represents the actual radio or television programme, and then to sort the signal out at the receiving end.

Radio waves are not interfered with very much as they pass through the atmosphere. Light waves, on the other hand, are easily bent and dispersed by the air. At present, their maximum horizontal range is only of the order of a few miles.

So the atmosphere along the surface of the Earth is not very promising. But upwards, towards other planets, or Earth-satellites, the atmosphere is relatively transparent. In fact, it is possible now to beam laser light at the Moon, and detect the beam of laser light reflected back. But for laser transmission on Earth, the signals would have to be transported through 'pipe-lines'.

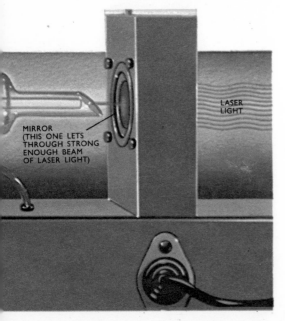

MIRROR (THIS ONE LETS THROUGH STRONG ENOUGH BEAM OF LASER LIGHT)

LASER LIGHT

CHAPTER SEVENTEEN

The Photomultiplier

IN a television camera, the energy of a beam of light is given to a beam of electrons. This is done for two main reasons. First the light must be represented by a pulse of electricity, so that it can eventually cause radio waves which can be transmitted. Secondly, the beam of light is not very powerful. The television picture is divided into a great many small pieces, so the amounts of light involved are small. They need amplifying. The photomultiplier does the job of first producing the electron beam, and then amplifying it.

A beam of light is made of minute

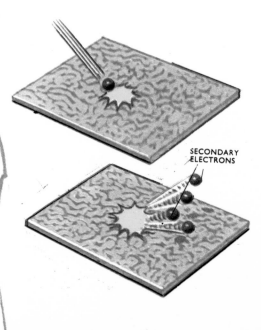

One energetic electron strikes the metal surface. Four less energetic electrons are knocked out.

SECONDARY ELECTRONS

Left: *a photomultiplier is used in this instrument for measuring street lighting.*

The Photomultiplier Principle.

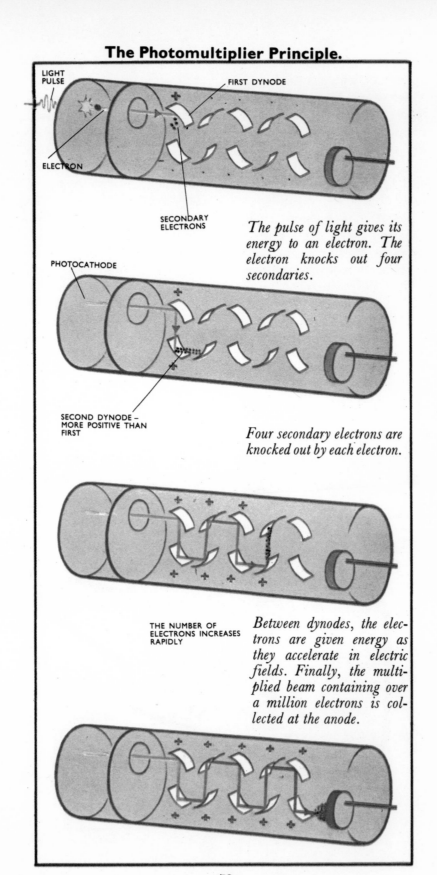

LIGHT PULSE

FIRST DYNODE

ELECTRON

SECONDARY ELECTRONS

The pulse of light gives its energy to an electron. The electron knocks out four secondaries.

PHOTOCATHODE

SECOND DYNODE – MORE POSITIVE THAN FIRST

Four secondary electrons are knocked out by each electron.

THE NUMBER OF ELECTRONS INCREASES RAPIDLY

Between dynodes, the electrons are given energy as they accelerate in electric fields. Finally, the multiplied beam containing over a million electrons is collected at the anode.

bundles, or photons, and each of these is capable of knocking an electron completely away from a sensitive piece of metal, the *photocathode*. The photon transfers its energy to the electron. As the electron leaves the photocathode it finds itself in an electric field. Electrostatic forces pull the negatively-charged electron away from the negatively-charged cathode (like charges repel each other), and give it extra energy as the particle is accelerated towards another plate.

When one electron hits this plate, it knocks several electrons away from the plate. The energy of the first electron is shared between the second batch of electrons, which are known as *secondaries*.

The secondaries are also accelerated by electric fields. They are attracted towards another plate (called a *dynode*), more positively charged than the plate from which they came and therefore capable of attracting the negatively-charged electrons. Again, at this plate, each electron releases several more *secondary electrons*. The electrons travel from plate to plate, each time their number being multiplied. If there are 10 plates and each electron releases four secondary electrons then by the time the electron beam reaches the final plate it consists of about a million electrons (i.e. 4 x 4 x 4 x 4 x 4 x 4 x 4 x 4 x 4 x 4 electrons).

This is the principle of the *photo-*

A cut-away view of the lighting meter. The upper part is the optical system for finding the right field of view. The lower part is the actual light-measuring system.

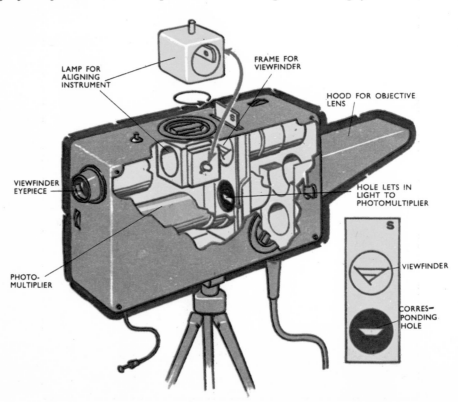

multiplier. Although the name means 'light multiplier' the beam of light is not actually amplified. Only the beam of electrons is amplified. The energy of the million or so secondary electrons comes from the repeated accelerations in electric fields, so the fields must be quite strong. The electric fields are caused by differences in voltage between the plates.

If the cathode is 'earthed', i.e. at zero voltage, the first of the *dynodes* is probably at about + 100 volts. The next dynode is at about 100 volts higher than this, i.e. at + 200 volts. The next is at + 300 volts, and so on. The anode, the final plate which collects the beam of electrons, is at a voltage of over 1,000 volts.

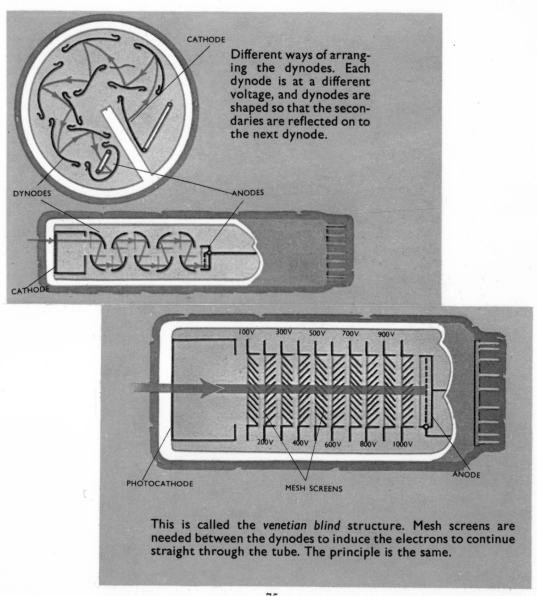

CATHODE

Different ways of arranging the dynodes. Each dynode is at a different voltage, and dynodes are shaped so that the secondaries are reflected on to the next dynode.

DYNODES

ANODES

CATHODE

100V   300V   500V   700V   900V

200V   400V   600V   800V   1000V

PHOTOCATHODE   MESH SCREENS   ANODE

This is called the *venetian blind* structure. Mesh screens are needed between the dynodes to induce the electrons to continue straight through the tube. The principle is the same.

75

CHAPTER EIGHTEEN

Television Aerials

TELEVISION aerials come in a wide variety of shapes and sizes. But in most of them the main part is a metal rod, divided at its midpoint, and made so that it is half a television wavelength long. It is called a *half-wave dipole*. The special cable leading to the television receiver forms the connection to each half of the dipole. Electromagnetic waves of all wavelengths are continuously sweeping past the aerial with the speed of light and inducing minute currents to flow to and fro along the

aerial. When the dipole aerial is about half the wavelength long, the current surges reinforce each other at all points along the aerial. In most aerials this happens not for just a single wavelength, but for a *band* of wavelengths, the width of which depends on the diameter of the rods making up the dipole. The maximum amount of radio wave 'space' taken up by any one broadcast is a band of frequencies eight million cycles per second (8 Megacycles per second) wide. The *bandwidth* of the aerial must

The Half-wave Dipole

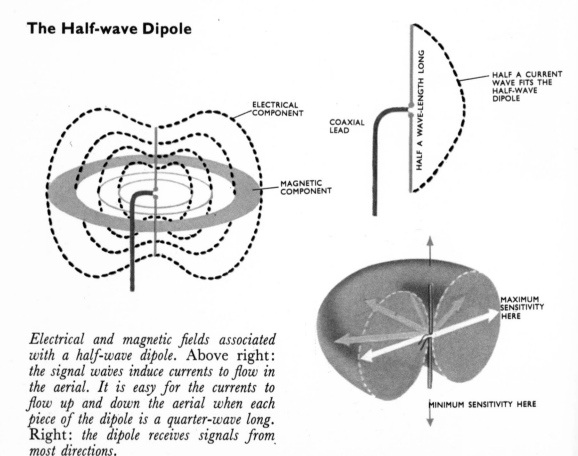

ELECTRICAL COMPONENT

MAGNETIC COMPONENT

COAXIAL LEAD

HALF A WAVE-LENGTH LONG

HALF A CURRENT WAVE FITS THE HALF-WAVE DIPOLE

MAXIMUM SENSITIVITY HERE

MINIMUM SENSITIVITY HERE

Electrical and magnetic fields associated with a half-wave dipole. Above right: *the signal waves induce currents to flow in the aerial. It is easy for the currents to flow up and down the aerial when each piece of the dipole is a quarter-wave long.* Right: *the dipole receives signals from most directions.*

be as wide as this.

The longest wavelengths used for television are about 21 feet long. It is usual to quote the *frequency* of these waves rather than their wavelength: the frequency of these longest waves is 45 million cycles per second. The dipole aerial to receive this signal is about 10½ feet long. Longer and shorter aerials can pick up a signal if they are near the transmitter, and the signal strength is high. The half wave dipole has, however, several advantages. It is an efficient aerial, and economical to make. It can also be used as the basis for even more efficient aerials.

If two nearby transmitters are both broadcasting at 45 million cycles per second, receiving aerials in the vicinity pick up both broadcasts, and are unable to separate them. The two signals interfere with each other. So neighbouring transmitters must transmit on different frequencies. The dipole aerials to receive them should have different lengths for efficient reception, although an aerial with a wide *bandwidth* may be able to receive several programmes if their difference in frequency is not great.

Aerials for one set of television channels may be between 10½ and 7 feet long. Aerials for the next set of television channels are perhaps three or four times shorter. It is

The Yagi Array

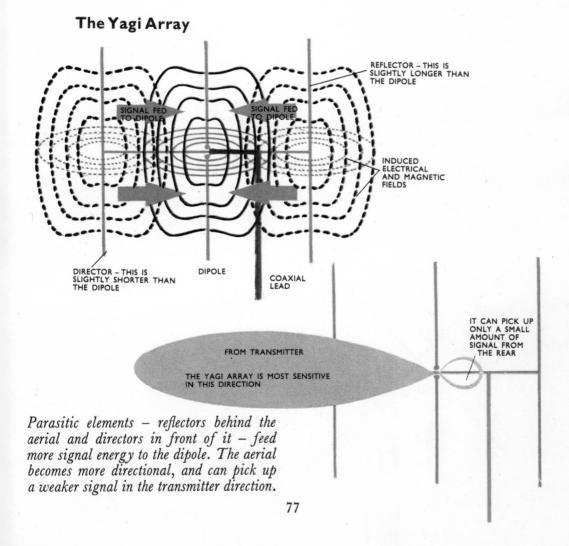

REFLECTOR – THIS IS SLIGHTLY LONGER THAN THE DIPOLE

SIGNAL FED TO DIPOLE

SIGNAL FED TO DIPOLE

INDUCED ELECTRICAL AND MAGNETIC FIELDS

DIRECTOR – THIS IS SLIGHTLY SHORTER THAN THE DIPOLE

DIPOLE

COAXIAL LEAD

IT CAN PICK UP ONLY A SMALL AMOUNT OF SIGNAL FROM THE REAR

FROM TRANSMITTER

THE YAGI ARRAY IS MOST SENSITIVE IN THIS DIRECTION

Parasitic elements – reflectors behind the aerial and directors in front of it – feed more signal energy to the dipole. The aerial becomes more directional, and can pick up a weaker signal in the transmitter direction.

77

the practice to use higher and higher frequencies, so the half-wave dipoles used become shorter and shorter. Ultra High Frequency (U.H.F.) dipole aerials are only between six and twelve inches long.

Reflectors and Directors

The half-wave dipole on its own is sufficient only where the signal is strong and there is no danger of reflections from surrounding buildings and hills. U.H.F. signals, especially, are distorted by surrounding obstacles, so a dipole alone is rarely used for receiving U.H.F. programmes.

Most dipole aerials have additional element or rods added to them. These are called *parasitic elements* because they are not in direct electrical contact with the dipole. But currents are induced to flow, to and fro, in them, as in the dipole. Electrical and magnetic fields are set up around each parasitic element, and energy is delivered to the

The 'X' aerial is a variation of the Yagi array, with a bent dipole and a bent parasitic element – in this example, a director. This aerial is most sensitive to signals dropping down towards the aerial.

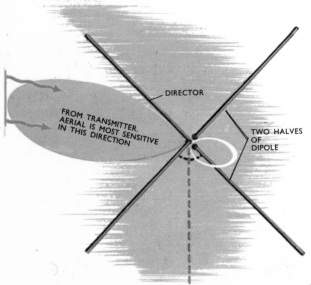

dipole through the fields. The signal reaching the aerial is increased. The aerial also becomes directional.

A parasitic element *behind* the dipole is called a reflector. It is slightly longer

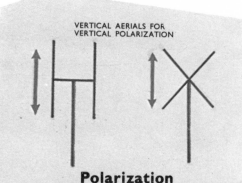

VERTICAL AERIALS FOR VERTICAL POLARIZATION

Polarization

Electromagnetic waves are variations in electrical and magnetic fields which travel with the speed of light. Generally speaking, the waves have an 'up-and-down' and a side-to-side component. Upright aerials send out only the up-and-down component – the wave is then said to be *vertically polarized*. An upright dipole aerial is needed to receive it.

If the transmitting elements are *horizontal*, the waves they transmit consist of only the side-to-side component, and are said to be *horizontally polarized*. A horizontal aerial is needed to pick up the horizontally polarized signal. Nearly all U.H.F. transmissions use horizontal polarization.

An upright aerial will not pick up a horizontally polarized signal, and *vice versa*. One method of avoiding interference between neighbouring transmitting stations is to make one send out vertically polarized signals and the other horizontally polarized signals. Then there is less likelihood of interference between them.

HORIZONTAL AERIALS FOR HORIZONTAL POLARIZATION

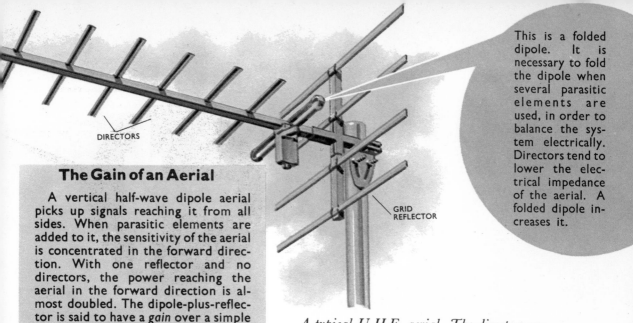

DIRECTORS

GRID
REFLECTOR

This is a folded dipole. It is necessary to fold the dipole when several parasitic elements are used, in order to balance the system electrically. Directors tend to lower the electrical impedance of the aerial. A folded dipole increases it.

A typical U.H.F. aerial. The directors are shorter than the dipole, and the reflector, in two parts, is longer than the dipole.

The Gain of an Aerial

A vertical half-wave dipole aerial picks up signals reaching it from all sides. When parasitic elements are added to it, the sensitivity of the aerial is concentrated in the forward direction. With one reflector and no directors, the power reaching the aerial in the forward direction is almost doubled. The dipole-plus-reflector is said to have a *gain* over a simple dipole.

The forward gain of the aerial is increased as directors are added to it. However, the increase per director drops as more directors are used, until it is not worth-while adding any more.

If the aerial is not well-designed, the gain can be increased in unwanted directions.

than the dipole. When the two are secured in position, the aerial becomes the familiar 'H'. The reflector prevents waves travelling towards the aerial from its side of the 'H'. It makes the aerial respond to signals from the front more than from the rear. It also improves the sensitivity, or *gain*, of the aerial in the forward direction.

Parasitic elements *in front* of the dipole are called *directors* and are smaller than the dipole. They increase the forward gain and make the aerial even more directional. An aerial with directors has to be carefully aligned in the direction of the television transmitter.

'X' aerials consist of one dipole and one director or reflector, attached to the support at their midpoints. Most transmitters are situated about 1,000 feet above sea level, so the main signal radiated away from them (the *space wave*) drops down towards the receiving aerial. An 'X' aerial with the

lower half of the dipole linked to the directors is sensitive to waves from above, but not from below, so it picks up only the broadcast waves, and not unwanted signals from the ground – for example, car ignition interference, or interfering waves from electric motors.

U.H.F. Aerials

Ultra high frequency signals have shorter ranges than the very high frequency signals. The shorter the wavelength the more likely it is to be absorbed or attenuated. U.H.F. aerials need more parasitic elements than V.H.F. aerials. Every additional director improves the forward gain of the aerial, as well as making it more directional. This helps to eliminate 'ghost' pictures, caused by reflections from surrounding buildings and hills.

The farther the aerial is from the transmitter, the more elements are needed to give a satisfactory picture. A typical U.H.F. 'fringe area' aerial has eighteen elements. One of these consists of a grid reflector mounted behind the dipole and the other sixteen are directors, mounted in front of the dipole. The type of reflector varies according to the designers' choice. Some have rods mounted in the form of a grid, others have a slotted plate or a wire mesh.

If a larger number parasitic elements is used, the aerial becomes cumbersome and heavy. The directors also affect the electrical properties of the aerial, and an increase in forward gain is offset by other factors.

Stacking two single aerial arrays side by side increases the directivity, forward gain, and bandwidth.

U.H.F. signals are more easily deflected and absorbed than V.H.F. signals, and behave very nearly like light waves. So their range is not so great. For this reason they require more complicated aerials for satisfactory reception. Because the aerial elements are so small, however, this disadvantage is offset – it becomes easy to make compact arrays which are very efficient. Also, the wavelengths are short and a given power at the transmitter will radiate a stronger signal. Compact and efficient arrays are also possible at the transmitting station.

As all the lower frequencies are already crowded, it is necessary to use the U.H.F. bands for new programmes in many countries. Each television programme takes up a band of frequencies from four to eight million cycles (4–8 *Mega*cycles) per second wide. A single television channel takes up a bigger band of frequencies than all the medium and long-wave broadcasts together.

When the transmitting frequency is of several hundred megacycles (U.H.F. frequencies) there are far more available channels eight million cycles per second wide.

INSET
ONE LEAD LEADS TO EACH HALF OF THE DIPOLE

The longest waves used for television broadcasts are about 21 feet long. The half-wave dipole aerial to receive these waves is 10½ feet long. The half-wave dipole on its own is omnidirectional – it receives signals from all directions. It can be used only when the signal is strong, and there is little danger of interference or echoes.

Different Types of U.H.F. Television Aerials

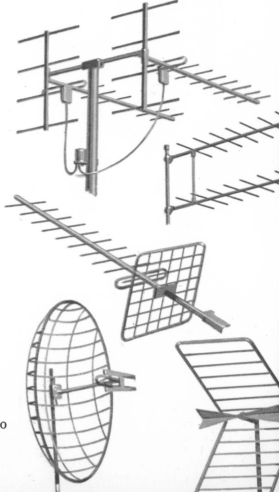

CHAPTER NINETEEN

Producing Microwaves

MICROWAVES are very short radio waves. Comparatively difficult to produce and to transport along a conventional wire, they nevertheless offer several great advantages as a means of communication.

Firstly, they can carry more information, more telephone conversations, more television channels than longer waves. This is why the already crowded longer wavelengths are being supplemented by microwave radio, television and telephone links.

Secondly, the short microwaves begin to behave more and more like light waves. When a microwave beam is directed at a solid object, the object reflects and scatters part of the beam, sending back an invisible radiowave 'picture' of the object. Longer waves would not send back a satisfactory 'picture' because long waves can sidle round objects small in relation to the length of the wave. Microwaves can produce good 'pictures', so they are used in *radar*.

Thirdly, it is easier to radiate

The aerials of a repeater station in an over-water television and telephone link. The stations, 20–40 miles apart, must be visible on the horizon. If it is not in the line of sight, it is not in the line of microwaves. The two outer dishes on the left produce vertically-polarized waves for the telephone link. The middle dish is the television link. Its microwaves are horizontally polarized.

Microwave devices are linked, not by wires, but by waveguides, *a form of electrical circuit 'plumbing'. The waveguide confines the signal, in the form of a wave.*

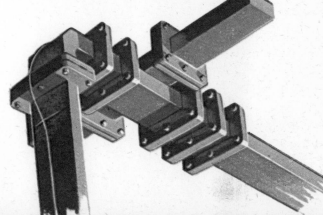

microwaves from aerials. For a given power input, the microwave aerial radiates a larger amount of power than a similar long-wave aerial. In fact, it is very difficult to contain microwaves within circuits and wires. The proportion of power radiated increases as the wave-lengths get smaller (and their frequency increases).

Television pictures are sent from one transmitting station to another as microwaves. Long-distance and international telephone links are using microwaves more and more. Microwaves are rarely transported in cables, because it is so much more efficient to beam them through the air.

With parabolic dish-shaped reflectors behind the aerial, the microwaves

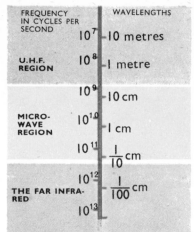

FREQUENCY IN CYCLES PER SECOND	WAVELENGTHS
10^7	10 metres
U.H.F. REGION 10^8	1 metre
10^9	10 cm
MICRO-WAVE REGION 10^{10}	1 cm
10^{11}	$\frac{1}{10}$ cm
10^{12}	$\frac{1}{100}$ cm
THE FAR INFRA-RED 10^{13}	

Microwaves start where ultra-high-frequency waves end. The longest micro-waves have a wavelength of around 10 cms. The shortest have wavelengths around a millimetre long. Electro-magnetic waves with wave-lengths longer than micro-waves are used for U.H.F. television broadcasts. The shorter wavelengths are verging on the *infra-red* part of the electromagnetic spectrum. Beyond the infra-red is the spectrum of visible light, and beyond this the region of ultra-violet waves and gamma rays.

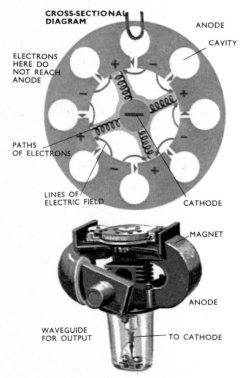

CROSS-SECTIONAL DIAGRAM

ANODE

CAVITY

ELECTRONS HERE DO NOT REACH ANODE

PATHS OF ELECTRONS

LINES OF ELECTRIC FIELD

CATHODE

MAGNET

ANODE

WAVEGUIDE FOR OUTPUT

TO CATHODE

A magnetron oscillator. This tube (valve) has a peak pulsed power output of 50,000 watts, at frequencies around 9,000,000,000 cycles per second (wavelength about 3 cms.).

can be radiated as a narrow-well-defined beam. In a microwave tele-phone link, for example, the micro-waves are beamed directly at the receiving aerial, a similar parabolic dish. No signal power is wasted by beaming it in other directions. The receiving aerial in the link would be between 20 and 40 miles away and less than a watt of radiated power can be detected over this distance. If this is just one section of a longer route, the receiving aerial is con-nected to a *repeater station* where the incoming signal is amplified to make up for transmission losses, and re-transmitted to the next aerial in the link.

Producing Microwaves

Microwaves cannot be produced by ordinary tubes (valves) or transistors. Electric current takes too long to travel through a tube. The tube oscillator 'feeds' a *tuned circuit* with pulses of energy, to sustain the oscillations set up in the tuned circuit whenever a current pulse is applied to it. At microwave frequencies, the tube gets hopelessly out of time, the oscillations are given energy at the wrong moment, and are forced to stop.

Several kinds of oscillator can produce microwave oscillations. As the use of microwaves increases, so do the new, improved types of microwave oscillator and amplifier. The *klystron* and the *magnetron* are elaborate types of tubes (valves). In the

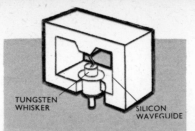

Silicon crystal diodes, with tungsten 'cat-whiskers', detect microwaves right down to the millimetre wavelengths. Tubes (valves) are sometimes used for high power detection. Another solid state diode, the *tunnel diode*, is being developed as a microwave oscillator. At present, its power output is limited to a few volts.

Microwaves in Research

Microwaves have played an important part in the study of the structure of molecules and crystals. Vibrating molecules and crystals in fact oscillate within the microwave region. The most accurate of all clocks, the *atomic clock*, depends on microwave vibrations – from caesium atoms or ammonia molecules.

A development of the microwave molecular oscillator is the microwave *amplifier* – it was discovered that some molecules store their vibrational energy, and then a host of molecules in the solid release energy at the same time. This produces a very narrow, amplified beam of microwaves. The microwave amplifier is called a *maser*.

From there, research has led to the *laser*, a development of the maser which produces light waves instead of microwaves.

klystron the electrons (which move relatively slowly in a conventional tube) are speeded up by ejecting them from a high-velocity electron gun. They travel in straight lines, and are picked up by an *anode*. But between the gun and the anode are two cavities, tuned to respond to a microwave frequency (as the cavities in musical instruments can be tuned to respond to particular audible sound frequencies). The first of these two cavities is the input. It naturally resonates at microwave frequency as a small amount of energy is fed to it from outside. The high velocity electron beam streams past the opening in the resonant cavity, experiences a varying electric field as a result of the oscillations there, and starts to 'bunch'. Some electrons speeded up by the field overtake electrons slowed down. The bunches occur along the high-velocity beam with microwave frequency. They impress microwave oscillations on the second cavity, feed energy into the cavity through an electric field, and, as a result, the second cavity is able to deliver microwave oscillations to circuits, or *waveguides*, outside.

Although most of the energy of the

high-velocity beam remains untapped, klystrons have been developed which generate a thousand kilowatts of power. These high-power microwave oscillators are used to cycle particles along atomic accelerators.

The magnetron is an entirely different design. As its name suggests, it contains magnets, and the oscillating electric currents in the magnetron are controlled by magnetic as well as electrical effects. Again, there are resonant cavities, typical of most microwave devices. Six or eight. of them are part of the magnetron's anode, and they are clustered around the cathode.

The magnetron is a very complicated tube (valve). Electrons from the central cathode are forced into tight spirals by the surrounding magnetic field. The electrons in the cavity in the anode tend to oscillate, and their mouths become alternately positively and negatively charged. The positive parts of the anode attract the spiralling electrons; opposite the negative parts, the electrons are forced to return to the anode, following a tight, circular path. All

the cavities interact with each other, but enough electrical energy is fed to the resonant cavities to sustain oscillations. There is no point in feeding oscillations at the wrong moment: they would be forced to die down. The dimensions of the magnetron are chosen so that this does not happen. The dimensions of the resonant cavities govern the wavelength (and the frequency) of the microwaves.

Other newly-developed types of high power oscillator/amplifiers are *travelling-wave tubes, backward wave oscillators* and *crossed-field amplifiers*. At lower power levels, the *tunnel diode*, a modified form of semi-conductor diode, can be used.

A high-powered klystron amplifier, capable of amplifying 10 cm. pulsed microwaves, and giving a power output of 8,000 watts. The input wave, a continuous signal, is only 3 watts and is fed to the first of three resonant cavities. The output is used in aerial navigation systems.

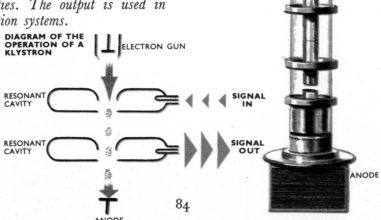

DIAGRAM OF THE OPERATION OF A KLYSTRON — ELECTRON GUN

RESONANT CAVITY — SIGNAL IN

RESONANT CAVITY — SIGNAL OUT

ANODE

ANODE

84

CHAPTER TWENTY

Waveguides

A SPYGLASS tube is a guide for light waves, a pair of solid electrically-conducting wires is a guide for radio waves. The cross between the two is a hollow, electrically-conducting tube, a *waveguide*.

Not surprisingly, this hybrid device is used for guiding the waves which lie between light waves and radio waves in the electromagnetic spectrum – the *microwaves*. Longer than visible light waves (and invisible infra-red waves), shorter than radio waves, microwaves are becoming increasingly important as a means of communication. The waveguide takes the place of the transmission line between the oscillators and the aerial.

No waveguide stretches for miles. Waveguides – accurately made, rectangularly cross-sectioned tubes of aluminium are expensive. It is usually better to transmit the microwaves in a narrow beam through the air. Microwaves can be focused like light waves, and concentrated in narrow beams.

A small amount of power goes a long way when microwaves are transmitted through the air. Half a watt of radiated power can be detected over a distance of 40 miles. Microwave telephone and television links operate on radiation power levels as low as a few watts. Radar power is usually much higher, because only a minute fraction of the radiated beam is reflected back to the microwave detector.

Diagonally-placed and off-centred slots, half a signal wavelength long, interrupt the field pattern and radiate signal energy away.

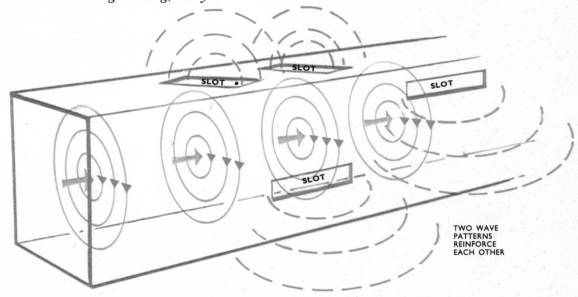

85

Below : the bent wave-guide extracts some of the energy from the straight guide. The guides are coupled by transverse slots.

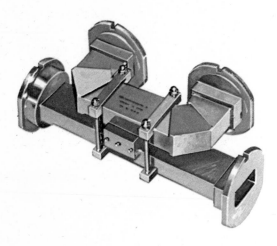

When an alternating electric current flows along a wire, magnetic fields are set up around the wire. The quicker the oscillations, the bigger the fields. Transmission lines for carrying the alternating signal occur in pairs. The second line of the pair also has magnetic fields built up around it. Electric fields between the two wires build up and collapse. The wires are really guiding an *electromagnetic wave*.

Some of the energy is bound to leak away (be radiated) and some is lost because the material spacing the wires is not a perfect insulator. The

Below : the waveguide horn acts as an aerial for incoming or outgoing microwaves. It can be used to feed a larger aerial, or for measuring aerial direction patterns.

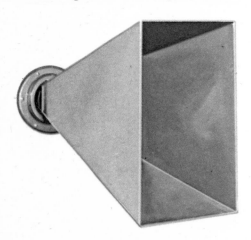

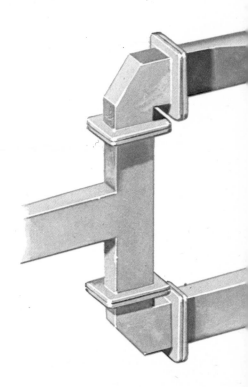

loss becomes more and more serious the quicker the current changes direction i.e. the higher the *frequency* of the guided wave. At microwave frequencies, greater than 3,000 million cycles per second, a pair of wires becomes very inefficient as a means of carrying signals from one point to another.

The two main reasons for inefficiency are (1) fields stray outside the

How does a waveguide work? The microwaves in the guide behave almost like light waves. If a lamp were placed at one end of the tube, some of its light would bounce from wall to wall along the guide, criss-crossing across the air-space until it reached the far end of the waveguide. If the tube is straight, some light waves can, of course, travel straight to the far end without bounc-

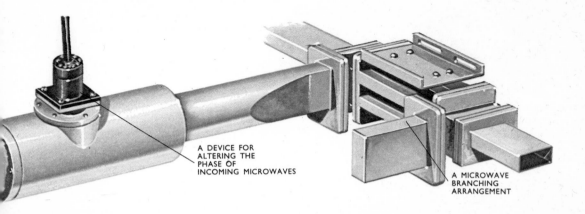

A DEVICE FOR ALTERING THE PHASE OF INCOMING MICROWAVES

A MICROWAVE BRANCHING ARRANGEMENT

This waveguide is part of the aerial feed of a microwave telephone and television link. Microwaves can travel around properly-shaped bends.

conductor, and some of their energy is lost (2) it is not always possible to space the wires with air (the two wires must be spaced apart by some form of insulator). Other materials, less efficient than air have to be used.

In waveguides, difficulties are overcome by (1) turning the two wires into a closed box, enclosing the fields and (2) there is no need for an inefficient spacer, because the sides of the waveguide are spaced rigidly apart. The space can be filled with dry air or evacuated where it joins an oscillator

ing. This, however, cannot happen to microwaves in a waveguide. The distance apart of the waveguide walls is between a quarter and a half a micro-wavelength. Disturbing things happen to all kinds of waves – sound waves and water waves as well as the electromagnetic variety – whenever the guiding tube is of roughly the same dimensions as the wave. Only a few wave-paths become possible. Most paths are ruled out because waves eliminate each other – wave crests have coincided with wave troughs, and

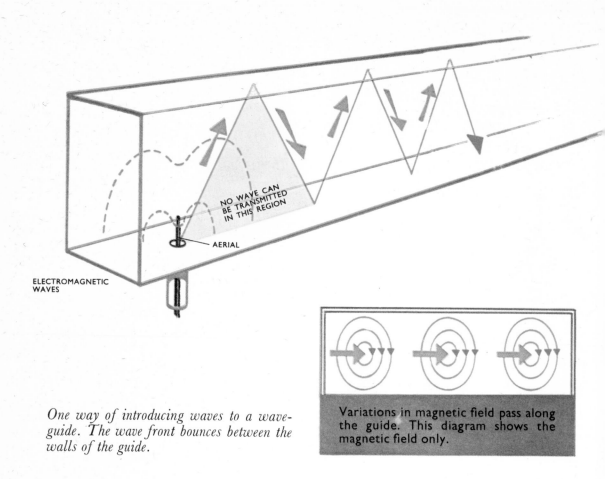

ELECTROMAGNETIC
WAVES

NO WAVE CAN
BE TRANSMITTED
IN THIS REGION

AERIAL

One way of introducing waves to a wave-guide. The wave front bounces between the walls of the guide.

Variations in magnetic field pass along the guide. This diagram shows the magnetic field only.

interfered destructively.

One end of the waveguide is coupled to a microwave oscillator, perhaps through a small 'probe' and an aerial which radiates microwaves as the lamp radiated light waves. The aerial radiates in nearly all directions, but only waves radiated at certain angles, relative to the waveguide, can criss-cross successfully to the other end.

Each time the wave 'strikes' the wall, magnetic and electric fields are set up in and around the wall, and electric currents are induced to flow to-and-fro along the waveguide. Current flows along the two of the sides of the guide (corresponding to the two wires of transmission lines), changing direction as the microwave changes direction, i.e. at the microwave frequency.

Certain conditions must be fulfilled. The wave is surrounded on all sides by a conducting metal tube. Lines of electrical field joining temporary accumulations of positive charge to temporary accumulations of negative charge must always be at right angles to the inside surface of the guide. The magnetic field, on the other hand, must lie parallel to the surface. Only a few waves can satisfy these conditions for a given waveguide. The wavelength of the wave is related to the diameter of the waveguide, and also to its length. The smaller the microwave, the smaller the tube diameter. A 10 cm wavelength microwave could be propagated along a rectangular waveguide of inside dimensions $2 \cdot 84 \times 1 \cdot 34$ cms. The waveguide for 1 cm microwaves would be almost exactly 10 times smaller.

Most waveguides have a rectangular cross section, but circular tubes are

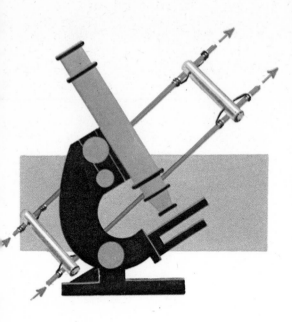

The waveguide is a cross between a hollow light guide and a pair of conducting wires.

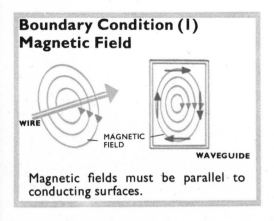

Boundary Condition (1) Magnetic Field

WIRE

MAGNETIC FIELD

WAVEGUIDE

Magnetic fields must be parallel to conducting surfaces.

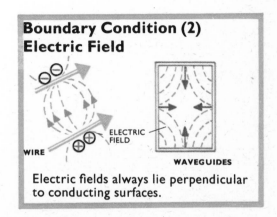

Boundary Condition (2) Electric Field

WIRE

ELECTRIC FIELD

WAVEGUIDES

Electric fields always lie perpendicular to conducting surfaces.

sometimes used. The waveguide is rarely a straight, uninterrupted tube. With care, the tubes can be bent to guide the wave round corners. When different circuits join on to one waveguide, extra rectangular and circular pieces are joined on. These can act as a short circuit (a *shunt*), a complete wave-path blockage, a high-power/low-power switch, and so on. Whenever two pieces of guide are joined together, specially-shaped cavities have to be made around the join so that the waves do not leak away.

Somewhere near the end of a waveguide is a slot, or a series of slots half a wavelength long. These are cut into the waveguide, and positioned so that they act as aerials to radiate the wave away from the guide (waveguides can be used in reverse – the slots then act as aerials for incoming microwaves). The slots are cut so that they disturb the waves in the guide *as much as possible*.

Radiation from Atoms and Outer Space

CHAPTER TWENTY-ONE

Nuclear Radiation

MANY nuclear reactors look huge from the outside, although the space occupied by the reactor itself is comparatively small. Lead and thick layers of concrete are built around the reactor to shield the workers outside from the dangerous radiation inside. The concrete layer is several feet thick. The best way of protecting against most penetrating kinds of radiation is to put a large amount of dense material around the radiation source.

The concrete and the lead are mainly to trap gamma rays, the most penetrating and dangerous forms of radiation. The energy of the gamma ray is absorbed by atoms in lead and concrete. The more atoms there are, the greater the chance that the gamma ray will be absorbed before it reaches

the outside.

Gamma rays are a form of *electro-magnetic radiation* – the rays are similar to visible light rays, but carry much more energy and are more powerful. Other common types of radiation are *particles*.

Alpha particles, the nuclei of atoms of helium, present few shielding problems. In air, they have ranges of only a few inches before they lose their energy in repeated collisions with air molecules. A sheet of paper can stop an alpha particle.

Beta particles (negatively charged electrons) are smaller. They carry only one unit of negative electric charge, and can usually travel farther before they are stopped. A sheet of plastic shields against most of the lower-energy beta particles. The thickness of

Alpha particles have only short ranges. Paper will stop them.

ALPHA-PARTICLES (HELIUM NUCLEI)

Beta particles are best stopped by lighter materials, such as plastic.

BETA-PARTICLES (ELECTRONS)

PLASTIC GLOVES IN 'GLOVE BOX'

the plastic shield depends on the energy of the beta particles. Faster beta particles, with more energy, require a thicker layer to stop them.

When beta particles are stopped in matter, part of their energy is radiated as a form of electromagnetic radiation called *Bremsstrahlung* radiation (Deceleration Radiation). Its energy can vary enormously, from practically nothing up to the maximum energy of the beta particles which caused the radiation. Bremsstrahlung radiation is far more penetrating than the original radiation, and it is an additional hazard when the amount of radioactive beta particle-emitting material is large. Heavy elements emit more Bremsstrahlung radiation than light elements, so this is why light plastic materials are most suitable to protect against beta particle emission.

Neutrons are very penetrating, and difficult to stop. They do not interact with matter because they carry no electrical charge. But some elements, notably boron and cadmium, absorb

Gamma rays are absorbed by thick layers of dense material. There is no simple explanation of how the absorption takes place. It is a mixture of three different processes.

1. Collisions with loose electrons.
The gamma ray collides with a free electron in the absorbing material. The gamma ray behaves almost like a solid particle, bouncing away from the electron. The result is a ray of lower energy than the original gamma ray. The electron takes some of the energy away from the gamma ray.

2. Collisions with bound electrons.
The gamma ray strikes an electron, bound by electrostatic forces to its parent atom. The gamma ray is completely absorbed and the electron is ejected away from the atom. This is the well-known *photoelectric effect*.

3. Producing new particles.
Gamma rays of very high energy can sometimes change into a pair of particles, a positive electron and a negative electron. The electrons are then absorbed by the shielding material.

neutrons readily. Where there is a danger from neutrons, a thin layer of boron or cadmium acts as an effective absorber.

A thick layer of heavy material may be a good shield, but it is a nuisance when an experiment is being carried out inside the shielded area. A few inches of transparent lead glass (glass containing lead) are usually sufficient to absorb most dangerous radiation. Lead glass is naturally much heavier than ordinary glass. It must, however, be *stabilized* – specially treated so that it is not blackened by gamma-radiation.

Zinc bromide solution is used for viewing port-holes through several feet of concrete. This brownish liquid is more transparent than glass to visible radiation, but it stops gamma rays.

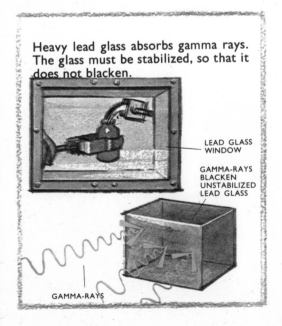

Heavy lead glass absorbs gamma rays. The glass must be stabilized, so that it does not blacken.

LEAD GLASS WINDOW

GAMMA-RAYS BLACKEN UNSTABILIZED LEAD GLASS

GAMMA-RAYS

CHAPTER TWENTY-TWO

Safeguarding against Radiation

WE can see light radiation and feel heat radiation. But none of the human senses can detect the ionizing radiation – alpha-rays, beta-rays and gamma rays – from radioactive sources and from particle accelerators. This invisible form of radiation is nevertheless capable of killing human cells and causing damage to human tissues. Ionizing radiation can be dangerous, and therefore special instruments must be used to take the place of the human senses in detecting the radiation.

In any area when radioactive materials are being handled, precautions must be taken, firstly to reduce the amount of direct radiation by 'shielding' the material, and secondly to prevent people from inhaling dust which may have been contaminated with the radioactive material. The first of these, where the material is outside the body, is called *external radiation*, and the second, where the radioactive contamination is inside the body, *internal radiation*. All establishments using ionizing radiation have special rules for controlling both radiation and contamination, and for ensuring that no one receives more than the maximum permissible dose of radiation. In large establishments there is a *health physics* department, concerned with advising with how best to keep radiation doses to a minimum, and with measuring radiation levels.

Radiation Levels

Shielding can reduce radiation to a low level, but never eliminates it altogether. There is no point in removing all traces of radiation, because low levels of it are certainly not dangerous to life. For thousands of millions of years *cosmic rays* have been reaching the Earth's surface, and giving rise to a constant background of ionizing radiation. Man has survived the background level, so obviously it is not lethal.

At what level does radiation start becoming harmful? Not enough is known about the effects of radiation on the human body to set definite limits. It is known, for example, that a dose to the whole of the body of about 2,000 rems is likely to be fatal. The *rem* is the most recent unit to be introduced for measuring the effect of radiation on the human body. In addition, two other units, the *roentgen* and the *rad*, are used for specialized purposes. On the *rem* scale, the amount of unavoidable background radiation caused by cosmic rays is 0·1 rem per year. In an average lifetime, a human being will absorb an absolute minimum of 7 rems.

The steady background of cosmic radiation is added to by the by-products of atomic explosions, which eventually come down to the Earth's surface. So the background fluctuates with the season and with the level of atomic testing. Once the background is known, sudden local increases in radiation can be detected.

A shielded container used for carrying radioactive material.

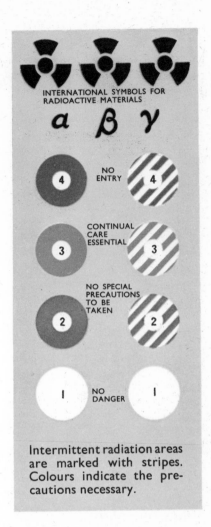

INTERNATIONAL SYMBOLS FOR RADIOACTIVE MATERIALS

α β γ

4 — NO ENTRY — 4

3 — CONTINUAL CARE ESSENTIAL — 3

2 — NO SPECIAL PRECAUTIONS TO BE TAKEN — 2

1 — NO DANGER — 1

Intermittent radiation areas are marked with stripes. Colours indicate the precautions necessary.

A dose of radiation can be built up quickly – for example, in the danger area of an atomic explosion – or it can be built up slowly over a number of years, as it is with the background radiation. Probably one heavy dose does more harm than the same amount of radiation absorbed over a longer period, but the exact correlation between the two is not known. Within limits, doses can be averaged out. Someone who receives a large dose through working in strong radiation for a short time is not allowed to work with radioactive material for a few weeks afterwards. The average dose over the whole period is thus reduced to less than the permitted maximum.

Somewhere between the background level and the 2,000 rem level, radiation starts having harmful effects. At present, medical experts agree that no person should absorb more than 16 rems between the ages of 18 and 30

while actually working with radioactive material. Younger people should not be allowed to handle radioactive material at all and the permitted levels for clerical workers and office staffs are lower, possibly because they do not have medical checks so frequently. With older people, there is less danger of genetical defects. So between the ages of 18 and 30, the maximum permissible dose is around 5 rems per year. This dose of radiation is not difficult to maintain, and will cause no detectable effect on the body during a person's lifetime.

In many atomic energy establishments, the average dose is much less

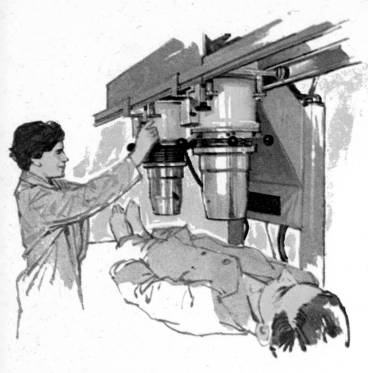

A whole-body radiation monitor, to detect and locate internal radiation.

than the maximum. For example, in one large establishment employing over 5,000 people, the average is 0·3 rem per year – only 3 times higher than the background.

Some radiation sources – for example, particle accelerators – can be switched off, and the radiation then stops. The danger from these sources is only intermittent. Radioactive isotopes cannot be switched off. Nothing can stop a radioactive isotope from giving off its radiation, so it must be shielded, and carried around in a carefully-designed, leak-proof container, usually containing lead.

Controlling Contamination

Radiation laboratories are always kept scrupulously clean, because accumulations of radioactive dust can lead to the spread of radioactive *contamination*. Once the dust has been breathed in, or has entered the skin through a cut, the source of radiation is actually inside the person, and it is impossible to get rid of it. Even the least penetrating forms of radiation could then damage the human tissues.

Most of the rules to prevent the spread of contamination are simply cleanliness routines. Workers keep special shoes to wear in the laboratory, and visitors wear washable overshoes. Radioactive dust is picked up by the shoes or overshoes and is not carried outside on the shoes of workers and visitors. Exposed areas of the skin must be washed when leaving an area with a high risk of contamination, and then 'monitored' by a machine which can detect the slightest trace of residual radioactivity. Special protective clothing (often made of plastic, which can be airtight and washable) and breathing apparatus is worn in places where the contamination is likely to be high.

All the water used for washing hands and protective clothing is specially treated to remove the radioactive elements. The effluent from any atomic energy establishment is monitored continuously to ensure that its radioactivity is below the approved level.

The air from fume cupboards, and so on, is filtered to remove the radioactive dust and fumes released in chemical and metallurgical laboratories.

Monitoring Radiation

A regular check is kept on the levels of external radiation and contamination in and around areas where there are sources of radiation. To measure external radiation and surface contamination, Geiger counters, scintillation counters and ionization chambers are used. These are the radiation-sensitive 'eyes and ears' of the health physicist. Contamination in the air is monitored by air and dust samplers. Some of these are modified vacuum cleaners. The vacuum cleaner sucks in a sample of the air in the radiation laboratory. Dust is trapped on a piece of filter paper. The amount of radioactivity deposited on the paper is later measured with a counter.

Small air samplers can be carried to record the amount of radioactive contamination breathed in by any individual. A small battery operated suction mechanism draws in air at a rate equal to the rate of drawing air into the lungs for breathing. The amount of contamination on the filter paper is then equal to the amount of contamination inhaled into the person's lungs.

Controlled Areas

Laboratories where the radioactive materials are actually handled need to be controlled more strictly than offices adjoining. Both are likely to be classed as controlled areas, with clear rules of conduct, but it is not necessary to have as elaborate control measures in the offices as in the laboratories.

Radioactive materials are kept in the tightly controlled areas, moved only when necessary, and then in special shielded containers. If there is a mishap and the radiation affects other areas, these areas are immediately cordoned off, and brought under strict control.

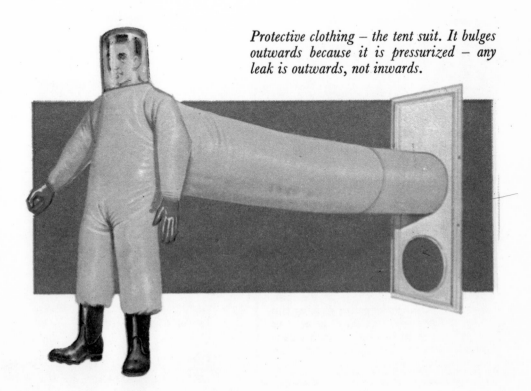

Protective clothing – the tent suit. It bulges outwards because it is pressurized – any leak is outwards, not inwards.

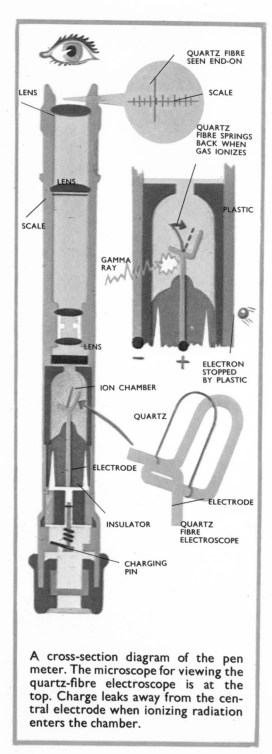

LENS

QUARTZ FIBRE
SEEN END-ON

SCALE

LENS

QUARTZ
FIBRE SPRINGS
BACK WHEN
GAS IONIZES

LENS

PLASTIC

SCALE

GAMMA
RAY

LENS

ELECTRON
STOPPED
BY PLASTIC

ION CHAMBER

QUARTZ

ELECTRODE

ELECTRODE

INSULATOR

QUARTZ
FIBRE
ELECTROSCOPE

CHARGING
PIN

A cross-section diagram of the pen meter. The microscope for viewing the quartz-fibre electroscope is at the top. Charge leaks away from the central electrode when ionizing radiation enters the chamber.

Everyone who works near a nuclear reactor, or who comes into contact with radioactive materials or X-rays, should carry a *dosimeter* around with him. The meter measures the dose of radiation received by the person carrying it.

There are two main types of meter. One looks like a fountain pen, and is clipped into a pocket. The other kind looks like a small badge. Both detect X-rays and gamma-rays. These are *ionizing* radiation. They apparently split up molecules in human tissue into *ions*, or charged particles, and the tissue becomes damaged.

The Pen Meter

The radiation also ionizes air molecules. Electrons are stripped off the air molecules, which then become electrically charged. The pen meter contains a small air chamber, acting as an electrical insulator between the outer wall of the pen and a piece of metal (an *electrode*) running through the centre of the chamber.

Before the pen is given to the wearer, the inner electrode is given an electric charge by connecting a voltage difference of 100–200 volts between it and the outside wall. Then the electrode is insulated so that it retains its charge.

High-energy radiation can enter the air chamber quite easily (less harmful lower energy radiation is prevented from affecting the meter by the thickness of the walls; this is a disadvantage because it cuts out beta-particles and very low energy X-rays which could still damage human skin). The radiation ionizes the air in the chamber. It momentarily releases electrical charges, the air stops acting as an electrical insulator, and becomes able to carry electrical charges. So some of the charge on the electrode leaks away through the air to the outer wall.

Each time radiation reaches the meter a bit more charge leaks away from the central electrode. Consequently its voltage gradually drops.

The voltage can be checked periodically, by measuring it with a sensitive electro-static voltmeter. However, some pens have a kind of voltage meter inside the air-chamber. This is a small piece of quartz fibre which springs away from the central electrode when it is fully charged (both fibre and electrode are similarly charged, and repel each other), and gradually springs back towards the electrode as the electrode loses its charge.

The rest of the pen meter is taken up by a small microscope, through which the quartz fibre can be seen.

The image of the fibre is projected on to a scale inside the microscope, which shows how much radiation has been absorbed.

If the voltage drops so much that the fibre moves beyond the end of the scale, the wearer may have absorbed more radiation than is considered acceptable, and may have to be taken off radiation work for a period. However, some pen dosimeters leak badly during wet weather (air containing moisture is a better electrical conductor than dry air), and the charge eventually leaks away from the electrode through the insulation at the end of the meter.

Although the film badge looks much simpler than the pen meter, it gives more information about the type of radiation encountered by its wearer. It is also sensitive to slow neutrons, which the pen meter is unable to detect. The radiation detector is a small piece of sensitive film in a light-tight packet which is placed inside the

Calibrating the film badges.

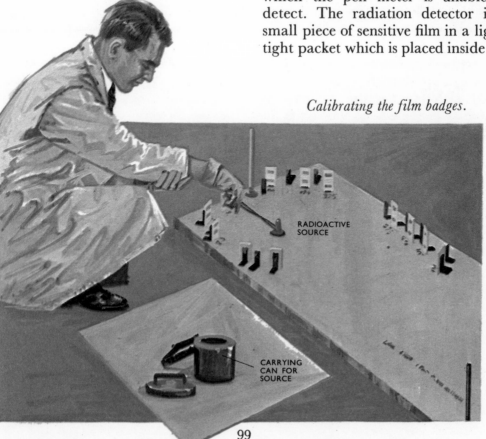

RADIOACTIVE SOURCE

CARRYING CAN FOR SOURCE

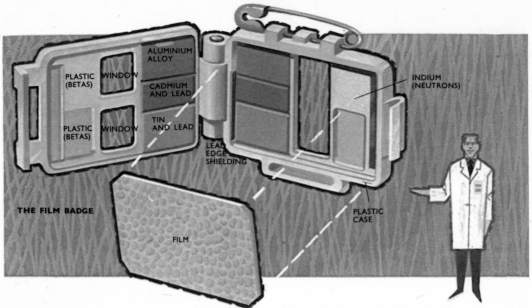

THE FILM BADGE

PLASTIC (BETAS)
WINDOW
ALUMINIUM ALLOY
CADMIUM AND LEAD
PLASTIC (BETAS)
WINDOW
TIN AND LEAD
LEAD EDGE SHIELDING
INDIUM (NEUTRONS)
PLASTIC CASE
FILM

badge. If radiation hits the film, it knocks electrons away from silver bromide atoms in the film emulsion, and this part of the film is ready to blacken when developed.

Filters at the front and back of the film stop one kind of radiation more than another kind. A plastic filter may stop beta-particles, but allow through gamma-rays and X-rays. When the film is developed, the part of the film behind the plastic filter can be compared with the unprotected part of the film, which has been exposed to all the radiation. The unfiltered part will be darker. The relative darkness indicates the relative proportions of beta-particles and gamma-rays.

Other filters can be of lead (which also cuts out beta-particles and most X-rays), cadmium and tin. Cadmium captures slow neutrons, and then emits high energy gamma-radiation, which affects the film. Neutrons on their own do not interfere with the film emulsion. The relative amounts of gamma-radiation and slow neutrons can be calculated from the blackening of the parts of the film filtered by cadmium and tin.

Indium is also used as a radiation

filter, because it absorbs slow neutrons and emits gamma-rays and beta-particles as a result.

The film packet in the badge is periodically replaced by a new one. The used film is developed and then compared with identical pieces of film calibrated by placing them at known distances from a radioactive source of known intensity.

Units of Radioactivity

Radiation does damage when it knocks electrons away from atoms (it *ionizes* the atoms). Radioactivity used

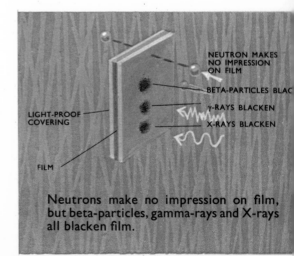

NEUTRON MAKES NO IMPRESSION ON FILM
BETA-PARTICLES BLAC
γ-RAYS BLACKEN
X-RAYS BLACKEN
LIGHT-PROOF COVERING
FILM

Neutrons make no impression on film, but beta-particles, gamma-rays and X-rays all blacken film.

to be measured either by the amount of electric charge produced by ionizing a known volume of air with the radiation (the unit was the *roentgen*) or by the amount of energy liberated as a result of the ionization (the *rad*). One rad imparts 100 ergs of energy per gram of irradiated material. This amount of energy is very small indeed – in fact, it takes 4.2×10^7 (42,000,000) ergs to heat one gram of water through one degree Centigrade. It is not the extra energy which is dangerous but the ionization.

Now a new unit, the *rem*, has replaced the *roentgen* and the *rad* in dosimetry. The *rem* is a measure of the biological effect of the radiation. *Rads*, *roentgens* and *rems* are practically interchangeable. A dose of radiation expressed in *rems* has about the same numerical value as a dose expressed in *rads* or *roentgens*. However, the units do sometimes differ, depending on the type of radiation, or on the type of material being irradiated.

A fatal dose of radiation is about 1,000–2,000 rems, 400–500 rems can be lethal if no medical attention is given, and radiation sickness can be caused by a dose greater than 100 rems. Even lower doses can increase the chance of contracting leukemia, or shorten the life-span. It is recommended that no-one should absorb more than 50 rems between the ages of 18 and 30, and the maximum 'safe' dose spread over a whole life-time is about 200 rems. So the maximum 'safe' dose per year is 4–5 rems.

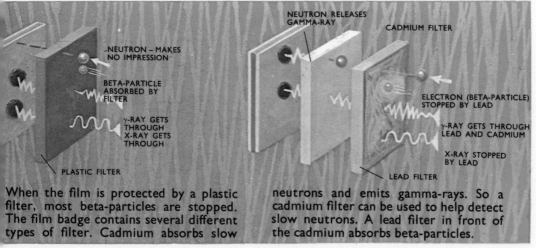

When the film is protected by a plastic filter, most beta-particles are stopped. The film badge contains several different types of filter. Cadmium absorbs slow neutrons and emits gamma-rays. So a cadmium filter can be used to help detect slow neutrons. A lead filter in front of the cadmium absorbs beta-particles.

CHAPTER TWENTY-THREE

Cosmic Rays and the Electron-Positron Pair

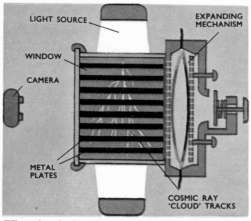

The cloud chamber (above) is adapted for cosmic ray research. Metal plates are necessary to slow down the powerful cosmic rays.

Below: Tracks in the 'nuclear emulsion' show an electron-positron pair.

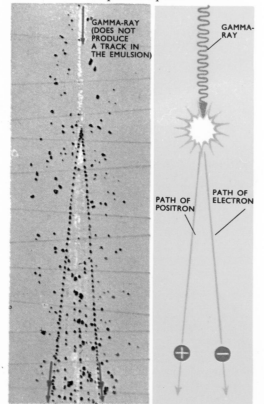

COSMIC RAYS

Light rays, X-rays and gamma-rays are all wavelike disturbances – electromagnetic waves. But the cosmic rays which are continually pouring down on the Earth are *particles* which come from inside and outside the solar system. The main reason for the great interest in cosmic rays lies in their incredibly high energy – far greater than that Man can give his artificially-accelerated particles. Most of the experiments using particles produced in machines like the proton synchrotron are concerned with finding more and more minute details about the structure of the nuclei of atoms. High-energy cosmic rays, donated free of

'Pairs' and conservation laws

Among the most important laws in Physics are the *Conservation Laws* which state that certain quantities can never be created nor destroyed; they must always be *conserved*. Mass, energy, momentum and electric charge are four of the most important quantities, and the production of an electron-positron pair from a gamma-ray is apparently violating all of them.

charge by unknown sources in the Universe, play an important role in these experiments, since the more energetic the particles used the deeper the nucleus can be penetrated.

There are two kinds of cosmic ray – primary and secondary. Primaries are the original rays which reach the Earth's atmosphere from outer space. They consist of 86% hydrogen nuclei (protons) and 13% helium nuclei (alpha particles), with nuclei of heavier elements, such as lithium, carbon, calcium and iron, making up the remaining 1%.

Primary rays rarely travel far through the atmosphere before colliding with atoms of the atmospheric gases to produce secondary rays. Since most of the primaries are travelling at almost the speed of light they can penetrate deep into the nuclei of the atoms and completely disintegrate them. Very energetic particles may be ejected and several new particles have been discovered among the remnants of these collisions. One of these is the *positron*, the positively charged counterpart of the electron.

The secondary rays which reach the Earth's surface are a motley assortment of particles resulting from an infinite variety of interactions. These consist of particles like the *hyperons* and the *mesons*, as well as electrons, positrons and neutrons. Associated with them are high-energy gamma-rays and X-rays.

ELECTRON-POSITRON PAIR

The particles which carry electric current through circuits are *electrons*. They are negatively charged particles. Although in some metals they are relatively free to drift through the spaces between the atoms, they are nevertheless bound to the atoms. In fact, they are attracted to the heavier part of the atom, the nucleus, because the nucleus carries a *positive* electric charge.

There are just two kinds of charges in matter, positive ones and negative ones. They have the property that like

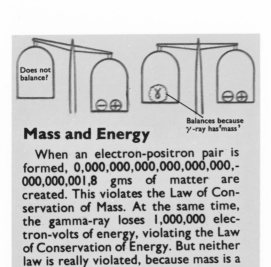

Mass and Energy

When an electron-positron pair is formed, 0,000,000,000,000,000,000,-000,000,001,8 gms of matter are created. This violates the Law of Conservation of Mass. At the same time, the gamma-ray loses 1,000,000 electron-volts of energy, violating the Law of Conservation of Energy. But neither law is really violated, because mass is a form of energy.

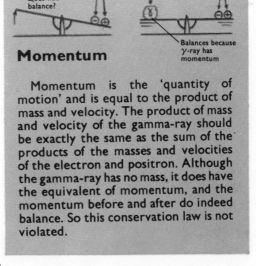

Momentum

Momentum is the 'quantity of motion' and is equal to the product of mass and velocity. The product of mass and velocity of the gamma-ray should be exactly the same as the sum of the products of the masses and velocities of the electron and positron. Although the gamma-ray has no mass, it does have the equivalent of momentum, and the momentum before and after do indeed balance. So this conservation law is not violated.

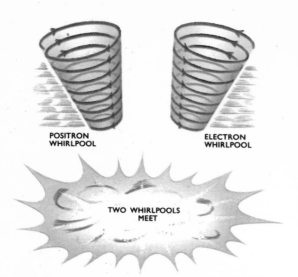

POSITRON
WHIRLPOOL

ELECTRON
WHIRLPOOL

TWO WHIRLPOOLS
MEET

Positrons and electrons are like whirlpools going round in opposite directions. When they meet, they annihilate each other.

whirlpools, of exactly the same size and intensity. The only difference between them is that the positron whirls round in one direction, while the electron whirls round in the opposite direction. Should they meet, the two whirls cancel each other, and the whirlpools are annihilated.

If they were all whirling round in the same direction, they would not do this. Since nearly all the electrons in matter are made to whirl round in the same direction, there is little danger of matter disappearing.

Producing a Positron

Practically the only way of producing rare particles like the positron is in a violent nuclear explosion. One nucleus is bombarded with another quickly moving nucleus, and the two nuclei may tend to coagulate (nuclear fusion) or disintegrate (nuclear fission). Smaller, lighter particles are usually ejected as a result. The heavier products of the explosion will probably be different elements, or different *isotopes*, but whatever elements are formed, the electric charges before and after the explosion must balance exactly. If there is too much negative charge after the explosion, then an electron will probably be ejected to get rid of it. If there is too much positive charge at the end of the explosion, the charges may be balanced by ejecting positrons.

The light metal beryllium will give out positrons when it is bombarded with alpha particles (helium nuclei). This reaction does not occur naturally – it is an example of *artificial radioactivity*. Several stages occur rapidly after one another, but the net result is that a nucleus of carbon-13 (the isotope of carbon with an atomic weight of 13) is formed. A neutron is ejected to

charges repel each other, while unlike charges attract each other.

Negatively charged nuclei are not likely to be found, but positively charged electrons, or *positrons* are more possible. They are very similar to electrons, having exactly the same mass and exactly the same size. The only difference lies in their charge. The positron is, however, a very rare particle. It is produced only occasionally and even then it cannot exist for very long. The reason is that negative electrons are the preferred variety in matter, and they are able to get rid of positrons fairly easily.

Electrons and positrons simply cannot exist together. If a positron collides with an electron, then both of them will probably be annihilated. They explode and disappear completely.

In many ways, the positrons and electrons do not behave like lumps of matter when they are near each other. Instead, they tend to behave like tiny

GAMMA-RAY

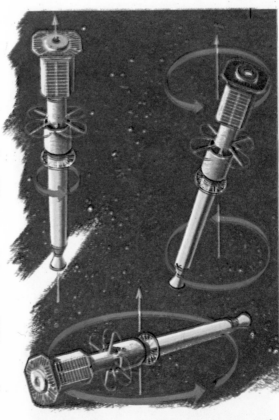

balance the masses before and after. The beryllium nucleus accounted for five positive charges before the reaction, and the alpha-particle for two. There is a total of seven charges before the reaction. But the carbon nucleus accounts for only six. To balance the charges and make up the extra positive charge, the only particle that can possibly be emitted is the positron.

Although this was the first convenient method of making them, the fact that the positron could be made had already been predicted mathe-

Explorer XI, used to detect gamma-rays in space. The crystal sandwich turns the gamma-rays into electron-positron pairs, which can be easily detected. Above: By rotating, Explorer XI scans the whole sky.

Electric charge

Two electric charges have apparently been created out of none (the gamma-ray is not a particle, so carries no electric charge), apparently violating the Law of Conservation of Charge. But no *net charge* is created, for the charges are of opposite sign, and cancel each other out.

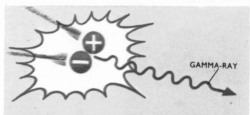

Annihilation radiation

A positron hits an electron, and is annihilated. The *annihilation gamma-ray* carries away with it all the mass (as energy) and balances the momentum. Charge is also conserved. There was no *net charge* before, and the gamma-ray certainly does not carry away any charge with it.

matically by the physicist P. A. M. Dirac. Then it was discovered among the remnants of more violent reactions

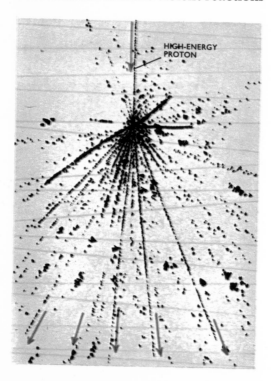

Stacks of special kinds of photographic plates, covered with 'nuclear emulsion' (right) are sent up into the atmosphere. The photograph above is pieced together from the many different layers. It shows a cosmic ray disintegrating an atom in the emulsion.

taking place in the atmosphere. As cosmic rays collide with atoms and molecules in the atmosphere, many different nuclear reactions may occur.

Occasionally, a very energetic gamma-ray is emitted. Gamma-rays are a kind of radiation like light rays, but they are far more penetrating and powerful. Sometimes, the gamma-ray is transformed into a pair of particles, an *electron-positron pair*.

This is possible only when the gamma-ray is energetic enough. Each of the particles, the positron and the electron, has a small mass, and the mass can be converted into amount of *energy*. Mass is a form of energy, but nuclear reactions are the only occasions when mass can be turned into

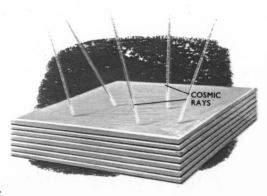

106

energy, or energy into mass. Positrons and electrons each weigh about 0·000,000,000,000,000,000,000,000,-000,9 gms, but this tiny mass is equivalent to about 500,000 electron-volts of energy. (An electron-volt is the energy gained by an electron when it is accelerated through a voltage difference of one volt and it is a convenient unit used to describe nuclear energy). The combined mass of the electron-positron pair is equivalent to about 1,000,000 electron-volts, so that gamma-ray can turn into an electron-positron pair provided it carries at least 1,000,000 electron-volts of energy. 1,000,000 electron-volts of the energy of the gamma-ray are turned into *matter*, and any remaining energy into kinetic energy of the moving particles. Actually, the gamma-ray needs to be carrying about 2,000,000 electron-volts of energy before an electron-positron pair is likely to be found.

Detecting the positron

When light strikes a photographic film, it causes chemical reactions among the light-sensitive atoms in the film. The same thing happens when particles strike sensitive films. Where they strike, they blacken the negative. For this reason, photographic film is often used to detect particles.

Special kinds of 'nuclear emulsion' have been developed for research. The sensitive particles in them are exceptionally small.

Particles which carry an electric charge blacken the nuclear emulsion far more readily than rays or particles which do not carry a charge. When, for

Huge balloons carry the 'nuclear emulsion' ▶
upwards to record cosmic rays.

107

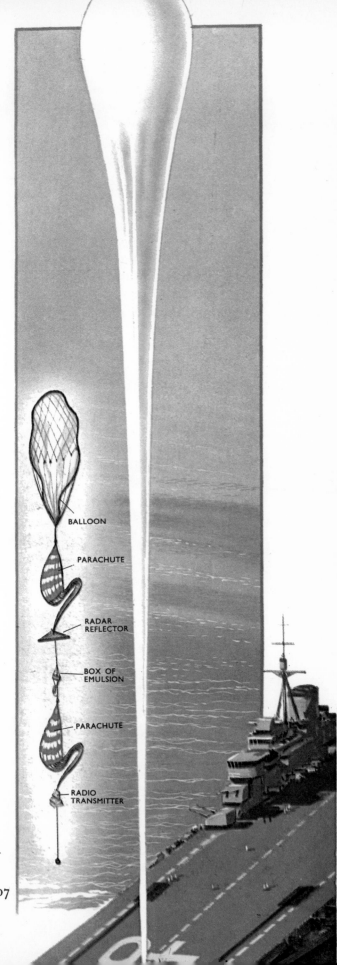

BALLOON

PARACHUTE

RADAR
REFLECTOR

BOX OF
EMULSION

PARACHUTE

RADIO
TRANSMITTER

instance, a high-energy gamma-ray travels through a nuclear emulsion, it passes unrecorded. It leaves no trail of blackening behind it. But if the gamma-ray suddenly turns into an electron-positron pair while it is in the emulsion, the event is clearly visible.

Two tracks, one the track of the positron and the other the track of the electron, appear from nowhere. The two tracks both start at the point where the gamma-ray disintegrated and they show that both positron and electron travel in roughly the same direction.

Nuclear emulsions are sent up on balloons to detect the particles in 'showers' of cosmic rays. It is of not much use sending up just one sheet of emulsion, for the chances of following the path of a cosmic ray in one are very small indeed. There is about as much point in 'fishing' for cosmic rays with one sheet of emulsion as there is in trying to catch a fish by dipping one small net and no bait in the sea. The fish may possibly swim near the net, but even then, it has to approach it in the right direction into the hole before it can be caught.

The layers of nuclear emulsion are stacked one on top of another to form a sizeable block. No matter from which direction the cosmic ray strikes the block, its passage will still be recorded in some of the layers of emulsion. In all probability, the track will run through several layers. When the film is recovered and processed, each separate layer must be carefully analysed and the complete tracks pieced together from fragments in different layers of emulsion.

Scientists can glean quite a lot of information from these tracks. They know how sensitive the emulsion is, and the sort of tracks each different particle will make in the emulsion. The tracks of electrons and positrons appear through a microscope as well-defined blobs, each one the result of a collision between the moving particles and a sensitive atom in the emulsion. From the distance between the blobs, scientists can tell whether the particles were in fact positrons and electrons, and also how fast they were travelling.

To clinch the fact that the tracks are the result of positrons, additional apparatus is needed. The only way of distinguishing a positron from an

A spark chamber. The track is a series of spark discharges through neon gas across the metal plates in the chamber.

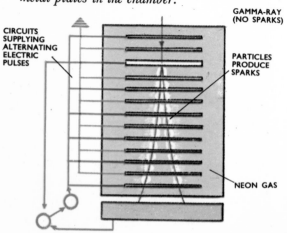

CIRCUITS
SUPPLYING
ALTERNATING
ELECTRIC
PULSES

GAMMA-RAY
(NO SPARKS)

PARTICLES
PRODUCE
SPARKS

NEON GAS

To produce the curved tracks of a pair, the spark chamber is placed between two magnetic poles.

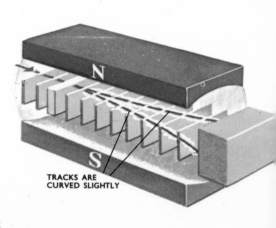

N

S

TRACKS ARE
CURVED SLIGHTLY

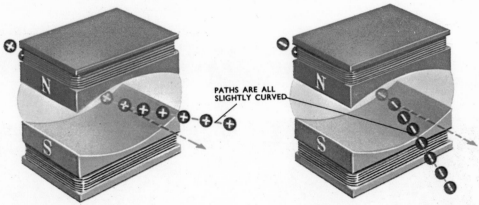

PATHS ARE ALL SLIGHTLY CURVED

A positron is deflected to the left in this magnetic field.

An electron is deflected to the right, while an electron-positron pair . . .

electron is by its *charge*. This makes a moving positron or electron behave just as though it were a wire carrying an electric current. Around it is a *magnetic field*. The magnetic field around a positron is in the opposite direction to the field around an electron, and, as might be expected, they behave in opposite ways when they are influenced by large magnets. The positrons will be deflected in one direction by the magnet and the electron in the opposite direction.

In one apparatus used in this kind of research, the *Spark Chamber*, large mag-

The 'pair' tracks in nuclear emulsions are straight when no magnetic field has been used.

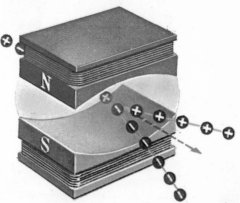

. . . produces two distinct curved tracks in a magnetic field.

nets are placed on either side of the chamber. Charged particles make tiny flashes of light or sparks as they pass between charged metal plates in the chamber, and their tracks will be curved because the magnets are deflecting the particles. Positron tracks are curved in one direction, and electron tracks in the other.

Cerenkov Counters

The Cerenkov counter is used only for high speed charged particles. In fact, the speed must approach the speed of light. The particle enters a transparent substance – glass, water, mica or cellophane. It must be travelling quicker than light

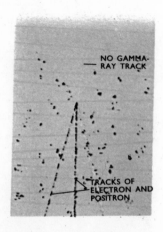

NO GAMMA-RAY TRACK

TRACKS OF ELECTRON AND POSITRON

travels in the substance (light travels more slowly in these denser substances than it does in air or in a vacuum).

Visible light is radiated from the path of the particle like the bow wave of a ship. The radiation is called *Cerenkov* radiation.

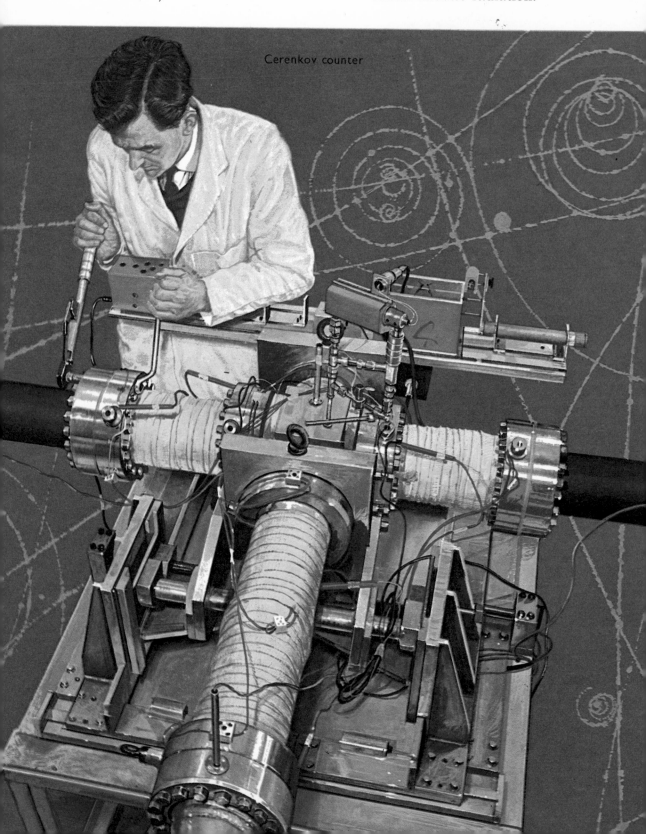

Cerenkov counter

Index